The Secret Forest

Text by Charles Bowden
Photographs by Jack W. Dykinga
Introduction by Paul S. Martin

A University of Arizona
Southwest Center Book

UNIVERSITY OF NEW MEXICO PRESS: ALBUQUERQUE

"Butterfly-Dog" reprinted by permission of J. P. S. Brown.

Library of Congress Cataloging-in-Publication Data

Bowden, Charles.
The secret forest/ text by Charles Bowden;
photographs by Jack W. Dykinga;
introduction by Paul S. Martin.—1st ed.
        p.   cm.
ISBN 0–8263–1403–1
1. Ethnobotany—Mexico—Sonora (State)
2. Forest ecology—Mexico—Sonora (State)
3. Indians of Mexico—Mexico—Sonora (State)—
     Ethnobotany.
I. Dykinga, Jack W.
II. Title.
GN564.M6B68   1993
581.6'1'0972'17—dc20
92–34880
CIP

Printed in Japan

The Secret Forest

Flowering amapa prieta and giant hecho cactus.

For John W. Hilton,
Howard Scott Gentry,
Ike Russell, and
the people of Sonora who taught them

Contents

Acknowledgments

THIS BOOK BEGAN ONE AFTERNOON in November 1990 when Paul S. Martin sat on my porch in Alamos sipping a beer and lamenting the on-going destruction of the dry tropical forest of southern Sonora. What you hold in your hands is a response to that lament.

The people of Sonora helped show the way, particularly Gustavo Aragón, Saul Enrrequez Figuora, Ramón Quintana, José Vallenzuela Gaztelum, Guillermo Zasueta Perea, and Teodoro Zasueta Corral. Merv Larson of Alamos helped time and again by getting me out into rough or seldom visited parts of the campo and by tolerating me as a guest in his Alamos establishment. The on-site cantina didn't hurt either. I particularly want to thank José Humberto Banoa Valenzuela and his four brothers, and his sister Ramona and their numerous kinfolk. They dragged me into the world of the campo, force-fed me venison stew and, all in all, taught me to smile no matter what the weather. Basically, anyone studying the dry tropical forest is merely reinventing a stock of knowledge that already rides easily inside the minds of folks like José Humberto. And I was graciously and repeatedly taught this fact.

Sandra Bruce Lanham piloted me to some of the worst dirt strips and most beautiful parts of the Sierra Madre. Mr. and Mrs. Delbert Lewis, Julian Hayden, *Phoenix* magazine, the Arizona-Sonora Desert Museum and the Robidoux Foundation supported the publication of this book.

The Southwest Center of the University of Arizona and its staff, Joseph Wilder, Carmen Villa Prezelski, and Karen Seger were essential in both raising the money for this book and nursing it along through the many bumps and grinds of putting the project together. In this day and age, it is difficult to raise money for a project such as this without an international tie. And it is difficult to find an institution that does not tie one down. The Southwest Center proved to be a perfect partner.

—CHARLES BOWDEN

I want to give special thanks for the production of the twenty limited edition dye transfer prints that constitute the traveling exhibition that accompanies publication of this book. This exacting work was generously done by Richard Jackson and Katherine Lampros of Hance Partners in Flagstaff, Arizona and Timothy Lewis and Beatrice Kime of Lewis Framing, Tucson, Arizona.

   Finally, my deepest gratitude to the Melody S. Robidoux Foundation Fund for their crucial support, both of this book and the traveling exhibit. Without their interest in Mexico and the environment, this project would not have been possible. Thanks.

—JACK DYKINGA

I want to acknowledge the editorial help of Julio Betancourt, Jan Bowers, Alberto Burquez, Angelina Martinez, Stephanie Meyer, Mary Ellen Morbeck, Mary Kay O'Rourke, Karen Seger, Jenifer Shopland, and especially the word-processing skills of Jo Ann Overs.

—PAUL MARTIN

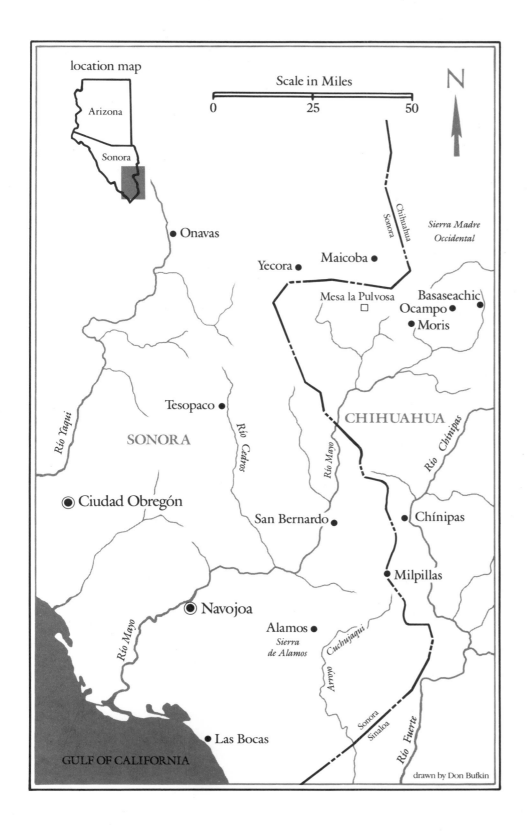

location map

Arizona

Sonora

Scale in Miles

0   25   50

N

Onavas

Yecora

Maicoba

Chihuahua
Sonora

*Sierra Madre
Occidental*

Mesa la Pulvosa

Basaseachic

Ocampo

Moris

Tesopaco

Río Yaqui

Río Cedros

SONORA

Río Mayo

CHIHUAHUA

Río Chínipas

Ciudad Obregón

San Bernardo

Chínipas

Milpillas

Navojoa

Río Mayo

Alamos

*Sierra
de Alamos*

Arroyo Cuchujaqui

Sonora
Sinaloa

Río Fuerte

Las Bocas

GULF OF CALIFORNIA

drawn by Don Bufkin

Treasures of the Sierra Madre

Treasures of the Sierra Madre

Paul S. Martin

June 1956: Where Barrancas Begin

WHEN COLONEL DAVIS MADE HIS OFFER I thought I'd simply turn it down. No more collecting trips south of the border. While I loved Mexico and field-work there, it had come to its logical conclusion, including a dissertation on one hundred animals: the frogs, salamanders, snakes and lizards found at the edge of the tropics in eastern Mexico. Puzzles about distributions of such animals led to questions that could better be tackled by studying fossils. I had another life to live.

The search could best be conducted in the adjacent deserts of the western United States. Well preserved perishable remains of both animals and plants and occasionally even dung of unusual animals such as the extinct ground sloths were or would be discovered in the dry caves of Arizona. Such depos-its were ideal for radiocarbon dating and for the ecological study of diet. They would reveal a new aspect of primeval America, of native megafauna, and perhaps even help explain the extinction cascade that struck large animals at the end of the last ice age.

Nevertheless, the more I thought about the Colonel's proposal, the more tempting it became. At no charge he would fly anyone interested in the northern Sierra Madre Occidental to his mountain airstrip near his mining claim, which lay over two hundred miles south of the border town of Dou-glas, Arizona. The alternative, to drive down there on rough mountain jeep roads, would take a week. It was a perfect opportunity to make some simple comparisons between the pine-oak forests at 31° North in Arizona's Chiricahua Mountains, where I was residing that summer, and those of 28° in Chihuahua, closer to the heart of pine-oak habitat in a part of the Sierra rarely visited by biologists. In addition, there might be caves in the canyons, caves with prehistoric fossils. Just possibly there could be dry cave deposits containing dung of extinct animals or ancient feathers of extinct condors like those found in a few famous caves of the Grand Canyon. There might even be fossil pollen in mountain *ciénegas* (marshes) revealing climatic changes of the last ice age. How could I resist? If the Colonel and I both dreamed of treasures in the Sierra Madre, they were treasures of a different kind!

To my astonishment, other residents that summer at the American Mu-seum field station outside Portal in the Chiricahua Mountains did not leap at the opportunity. While somewhat interested, they could not be diverted from their research. Some had to make periodic observations on the behavioral ecology of the local termites, moths, kangaroo rats, gray-breasted jays or long-nosed bats. Cave Creek in the Chiricahuas is beautiful. Why leave it on a wild goose chase into Mexico? In addition, in the case of those who had never been into the interior, I began to suspect closet cases of borderphobia. To some, just the prospect of filling out papers across the desk from an unsmiling uniformed Mexican immigration official sporting a Pancho Villa mustache is spooky. Who wants to take chances in a remote part of a Third World country whose legal system, when it can be applied, stems from the Napoleonic Code? And finally what about the hazards of mountain bush piloting? Don't those guys have a death wish? For whatever reason, there were no other volunteers. It turned out the Colonel didn't bother with papers when he flew to La Pulvosa.

I packed my field kit—cotton, wire, and thread for stuffing mammals, traps for catching them, formaldehyde and jars for preserving snakes, lizards, and frogs, and blotters for pressing plants. It would be one last, brief, blood-and-mouse-guts collecting trip, I promised myself and my wife and kids, one last good-bye to the Sierra Madre before turning to more serious investigations like the search for dry cave fossils north of the border. I didn't reckon on the power of the land where the barrancas begin. Any Apache could have predicted the outcome.

We left Douglas International airport on a bumpy flight over broken country, the air and the ground below both growing considerably rougher as we flew deeper into Sonora. Fighting nausea with limited success, I glimpsed out the cabin Plexiglas. Somewhere down below, the tropical trees of northern Mexico (including rock figs, Ures palms, mauto, pochote, palo santo, tepeguaje, and palo chino) battled to hold their northern limit, advancing or retreating through the centuries while dwarfed by drought, pruned by frost, and buffeted by temperate competitors. At our cruising elevation, ninety-one hundred feet, I could only imagine details of the timeless struggle. Down there, along the western margin of the Sierra Madre and east of the desert, a dozen kinds of tropical trees maintained themselves hundreds of miles north of the Tropic of Cancer, and five degrees of latitude further north than their relatives in eastern Mexico.

The reason why tropical trees range farther north in western than in eastern Mexico is the milder winter climate of Sonora. El Norte, an outburst of frigid polar air, regularly pours down out of the Arctic into western Canada and onward far beyond the foot of the Rockies and freezes the Gulf coastal plain of eastern Mexico, occasionally as far south as Veracruz, south of the Tropic of Cancer. El Norte bypasses the west coast. In the Sonoran lowlands winter nights may bring frosts. Light most of the time, they are on occasion heavy enough to damage the mangroves north of Kino Bay or kill the tops of guásima near La Barranca, but the icy blasts of El Norte do not storm down Mexico's west coast with anything like the frequency or ferocity experienced in south Texas and Tamaulipas, well south of the latitude of Sonora.

Over Yecora, a large mountain town and lumber mill on Sonora's side of the Sierra, we began a gradual descent. The Colonel pointed ahead, to where the land sank down toward the Río Mayo. While the drop, over four thousand feet of relative relief in four miles, is modest by the standards of west-coast Mexican barrancas, it portends even more spectacular rims beyond. Perched on the edge of the barrancas at sixty-five hundred feet in elevation, his airstrip on Mesa La Polvosa (dusty mesa) was surrounded by rich, uncut pine-oak forest.

By rights, since we had flown south on the Sonoran side, almost paralleling the Sonora-Chihuahua border, which runs north and south, we should still have been in Sonora. Nevertheless, for some mysterious reason a triangular jumble of basalt-capped mesas, six to seven thousand feet high and gouged by deep canyons draining southward into the Río Mayo, was gerrymandered out of Sonora into the State of Chihuahua. As far as I can see, the boundary wanders aimlessly across mountains and barrancas, blithely disregarding rivers, peaks, drainage divides, latitudes, longitudes or any other natural or geometric logic. Even the new topographic maps carefully plotted from aerial photography don't attempt to show the state line; only local ranchers seem to know where it really is.

Vital to learning the botanical secrets of the Sierra was another invisible boundary line we had crossed. We were slightly south of the parallel of 28.5° North, at the latitude of Corpus Christi, Texas and Tampa, Florida. We were also just south of the Río Yaqui drainage within the watershed of the Río Mayo and near the northern limit of tropical dry forest. We had entered the botanical world of Howard Scott Gentry. His remarkable book, *Río Mayo Plants,* published in 1942, has provided naturalists with the best introduction to the region. *Río Mayo Plants* was in my pack and would return with me on many more trips.

North of the border few people pay much attention to their native trees, shrubs and medicinal herbs. In contrast, the Sonorans and Chihuahuans living off the land are experts. Howard Gentry took advantage of their knowledge; in his fieldwork he learned a great deal about ethnobotany by talking to the natives, including the Warihio and other Indians. Increasingly, the lure of cities and towns, the need to educate children in school and, not least, the hazards of the drug wars are among a variety of forces working to depopulate the Sierra. Nevertheless, when you find them, the country people remain the best interpreters of their plant and animal resources.

Gentry's collecting localities lie between 28.5° and 26.5° North and 110°

and 108° West, a quadrangle of some sixteen thousand square miles, roughly twice the size of Massachusetts and only slightly smaller than Costa Rica. About half the land is low lying and tropical, supporting thorn forest and tropical deciduous forest. The mountains above are semitropical or temperate, with oaks (twenty species), pines (nine species) and madrone (two species). From his collections made in the 1930s, Gentry reported over twelve hundred species of vascular plants; subsequent work by him and others suggests the region harbors at least two thousand. New species are being discovered in remote and unexplored canyons and on bare rock of cliffs. Even more accessible places along roads may harbor novelty.

We were landing, finally. Skimming the trees next to a clearing, the Piper Cherokee was low enough to allow the pilot to eye the strip at close range. Satisfied that no cows or burros blocked our path and that no recent storms had gouged fresh runnels, he turned the plane into a final approach, its flaps fully extended, nose up and stall indicator screeching as the wheels bounced on the dirt.

Much relieved to be down on the ground and on good terms with my stomach again, I peered around to see what was outside. Flashing by beside the runway were round crowned trees, evenly spaced, with a dense foliage of big leaves suggesting mango trees. Surely, at this elevation we were not in a mango orchard!

Before I could solve the mystery, we had taxied to a rustic hangar of stacked pine logs. The Colonel introduced his manager, Juliano Rodriguez, and unloaded my sleeping bag and kit. It was late in the afternoon; thunderheads threatened. Leaving me to get my bearings, Colonel Davis departed immediately for business in Ciudad Obregón, promising to return in a few days.

I walked back along the runway to inspect the big-leaved trees. Indeed they were not mangos. They were vigorous young oak trees, released from competition after the clearing of the taller pines along the strip. *"Encino güeja,"* Juliano called them after their large cupped leaves shaped like a small bowl. No oaks like these grew in the Chiricahuas. On subsequent days spent tramping the woods, Juliano showed me three other oaks that do not reach Arizona, plus two (blue oaks and Arizona oaks) that do.

Encino güeja is also applied to another oak tree with even larger dished leaves, some as big as a soup bowl and some too big to fit in a plant press without trimming. Recently I learned from Richard Spellenberg, a botanist at New Mexico State University, that the oak I'd collected, with somewhat smaller cupped leaves, has long been confused with its relatives and is actually still undescribed! I find it hard to believe that a common oak tree, widespread it turns out, in the northern parts of the Sierra Madre at six to eight thousand feet in elevation, and the first tree I spotted on my initial trip into the Chihuahuan Sierra, is just now being anointed with its own proper scientific name!

The woods yielded other delights—flocks of thick-billed parrots by day, wild turkeys gobbling around the Colonel's hangar at dawn and dusk, whippoorwills in the night and fresh scratch marks on the ground near the alders at a low pass a mile away. Juliano attributed the marks to *lobos* (wolves). "They are the size of a police dog; they hunt deer and heifers," he added. Most of all I was drawn to the smoky dry-season sunsets on the rim looking south over the mountains. The low country is tropical and was largely leafless at the end of the dry season; the high country is temperate and, despite the drought, was stubbornly evergreen, all of it rolling on across the Río Mayo and up again into more mountains in a vast topographic jumble of wildness toward and beyond Arechuibo, according to Juliano, the "capital" of the Warihio Indians.

Thirty years later I finally went back with some friends to revisit Mesa La Polvosa, guided by Jaime Sanchez from Talayotes. Virgin pines, wolves, and the Colonel are all long gone. The airstrip, a pawn in the drug wars, was ditched and rendered inoperable by the Mexican army and is overrun with bracken ferns. The Colonel's hangar and house slowly decay. Nevertheless, the view south from the rim down into the wild roadless maze of tropical dry forest beneath the zone of evergreen oaks and threaded by the Río Mayo still beckons as powerfully as ever.

May 1960: To Moris for Fossil Sloth Dung

Although my flight with the Colonel had yielded no fossils, I learned that there were caves in the barranca country. Soon after moving to Tucson, I met a retired rancher, Ike Russell, who had taught himself to fly and was making trips to mining claims in the Sierra belonging to his friend from college days at the University of Arizona, Major William Swan (retired). A Mexican miner working gold claims outside Moris, Chihuahua told Ike about caves that he thought might yield fossil bones.

Besides, having gazed across it from Mesa La Polvosa, I knew I wanted to see the tropical part of the Río Mayo country firsthand, to see what grew down there, especially in a place that botanists apparently had seldom, if ever, visited. Howard Gentry's map indicated that, although it was in his study area, he had not been to Moris himself. The prospect of a reconnaissance trip into the upper Río Mayo country was inviting.

To help share expenses and adventures, Ike invited his friends, Art Almquist and Daphne Straub, to join us. With our sleeping bags, camping gear and a plant press, we all squeezed into Ike's potbellied, tail-dragging Aeronca Sedan. Tail draggers, Ike said, are preferred to the tricycle gear for rough field taxiing. The Aeronca, he added, was well-thought-of for its short-field performance. It could lift off easily with a full load despite its modest power plant, as he soon demonstrated.

Then we slowly floated upward, gradually gaining altitude, at a ground speed not much faster than one might expect from a loaded school bus. Once aloft, cruising speed was ninety miles an hour, a slim margin against the strong southwest winds to be expected many afternoons in the spring dry season in northern Mexico. From Tucson, it took us over four hours of flying time to reach Yecora, where we would spend the night, not including time on the ground in Hermosillo clearing customs. I began to wonder what I had gotten into. How good a plane was the Aeronca Sedan and how good a pilot was this ex-rancher?

My apprehensions increased on the walk to town from the Yecora airstrip when my eye caught sunset reflections from broken pieces of metal. There were parts of an airplane (a Taylorcraft it turned out) decorating various backyards. Here a strut or a wheel might be seen, there a tail section or an engine cowl.

"Ike," I asked, "whose airplane was that?"

"Mine," came the laconic reply.

Only years later did I get up the courage to ask about details of the crash. Ike had smashed his jaw and lost front teeth on a wobbly landing that Bill Swan blames on a loose raincoat fouling the control wires in the baggage compartment. Other details can be found in *Desert Quest,* a delightful new book about Yecora and the Yaqui River country by one of Ike's friends, the rancher-ornithologist-philanthropist, Randolph (Pat) Jenks. Pat happened to be in Yecora at the time and salvaged the engine of the Taylorcraft for Ike, returning to Tucson with it in the trailer of his jeep. Obviously the accident had not deterred Ike or his partner, Bill Swan, from further trips. News of the crash might well have deterred me. It was too late now.

The next day a cursory inspection of caves outside Yecora yielded nothing of interest, and that afternoon we resumed our flight to Moris, our main destination. We decided that a seven-thousand-foot round peak, just behind Mesa La Polvosa, was the highest point on the western rim of the Río Mayo country. Mountains loomed in all directions, except for one small valley to the east.

In it lay Moris, nestled five thousand feet below adjacent peaks and watered by tributaries of the Río Mayo. Half the size of Yecora, Moris features well-built, thick-walled old adobe homes around a town square that is enhanced by a fine stone church. Warihio hats made of *sotol (Dasylirion)* can be bought locally. In 1960, the nearest road ended thirty kilometers away at the mining town of Ocampo, four thousand feet higher up in the Sierra. We were told that from Ocampo, the drive to Chihuahua City took two days. All goods from Ocampo to Moris had to come down the mountains by pack mule.

In 1927 J. Frank Dobie rode horseback this way with a treasure hunter, C. B. Ruggles, both in search of the lost mine of Tayopa in Sonora. According to Dobie, the route from Chihuahua City through Ocampo to the Yaqui towns in Sonora was the *camino real*—the "royal road" of the early Spanish and a route undoubtedly long used by Indians before them. "From the mountains overtopping Ocampo snowclad in wintertime, it pitches down a mile in half a day's ride to the torrid level of oranges growing along the Mayo River and wild-cotton trees with thorn-studded trunks sticking out of its cliffs" *(Apache Gold and Yaqui Silver, 187).*

Built in 1934, the airstrip was reasonably well graded and fenced against livestock. There are a few corn fields around Moris, irrigated by runoff from arroyos in flood season, and the stores carried locally grown oranges, but most economic activity is focused on mining and ranching.

In town, Ike located his friend, Gerardo Carmargo. For our explorations Gerardo would help find a guide and *bestias* (pronounced "véstias," literally meaning "beasts," horses, mules, burros or even oxen, I suppose; Frank Dobie says early Spanish priests rode oxen); we needed four.

The tropical woods around Moris are low, thorny and arid, almost too dry to be considered tropical deciduous forest. Except in the summer rainy season, grass is sparse, and we were near the end of a long droughty spring. The only uneaten grasses found sanctuary beneath piles of spiny acacia branches left by wood choppers or defied the reach of their herbivorous foes from pockets of soil on the top of boulders. Gerardo did his best, but the four beasts he finally assembled for us were gaunt and weak, *muy flaco*, he admitted. If there were any fatter animals, they must have been pasturing in the grassy pine forests in the cool mountains above Ocampo.

The trail north out of town led along a pretty arroyo into permanent water at Santa Maria, where there were many trees new to me. One I recognized from the *tierra caliente* in eastern Mexico is a low spreading tree with foliage like an elm. *Guásima* the natives call it. Its scientific name, *Guazuma*, is obviously derivative. How one wishes for more of this! Such a practice would make the matter of learning scientific names of plants so much easier.

There were thickets of tropical hackberries *(garabato)* along the stream. They made a tangle of branches wickedly armed with hooked thorns like cat claws. There were sycamores *(aliso)* in a more tropical setting than I had seen them in before. The handsome tree *(pochote)* whose fruits yield kapok

(Dobie's wild cotton tree) and a low thorny tree common by the airstrip called *papache (Randia)* were both covered with white flowers. Although there were no sahuaros to be found any closer than in the foothills outside Cuidad Obregón one hundred miles to the southwest, there was an even taller columnar cactus supporting many fluted pipes that rise out of a sturdy trunk, the *hecho (Pachycereus)* or aborigine's comb, named for its bristly fruit.

As we rode by them outside Santa Maria, I somehow overlooked the yellow and red bald patches on the hillside. Surrounded by dry tropical forest, the bare red soils support little but oaks and *jarilla* (hop bush, *Dodonaea)*, which I did see and collect. On the red soils, the oaks and, at slightly higher elevations, pines grow below their expected lower elevations. Much later I realized that in Sonora near Rancho El Tablon, outside Tesopaco, Howard Gentry had discovered this phenomenon. In *Río Mayo Plants* he briefly mentions oaks surrounded by tropical forests where oaks would not be expected thanks to the red soils.

By evening we had arrived at Rancho Saucitos, which was named for its willow tree. A tiny irrigation ditch looked inviting and Daphne led the way to a rustic bath soon shared by her companions.

The next day saw us on the trail again, and the bestias were dragging their feet. We climbed out of the tropical lowlands into oak woodland. One oak is easily recognized by its distinctive long, hairlike bristles extending beyond the margin of its large shiny, tapering leaves. This is the *kusi,* a relative of the Emory oak of Arizona and Chihuahua. The Warihio Indians consume the raw acorns in season, which is mid-summer. Effete Anglos find them somewhat bitter.

Besides the kusi, there were willow-leaved oaks and Arizona oaks. Small pines appeared; scattered among them were low palm trees. The tops of cliffs supported two-meter-tall candles, the golden-yellow flowering stalks of octopus agave *(amole).* The stalks were in fruit at the base, in full bloom in the middle, and budding at the top. A tropical touch was added by the sweet-scented white flowers that Daphne found on a leafless stubby low tree or shrub, the *suchil,* a close relative of the frangipani *(Plumeria)* of the tropics. Our bestias had some strong botanical inclinations of their own; they tugged against the reins to snatch mouthfuls of *cola de ratón* (mountain muhley) and other perennial bunch grasses growing along the trail.

By midafternoon we had arrived at our destination, Cuevo de los Muertos, a big rock shelter with a flat floor overhung by yellow volcanic tuff. Cow manure strewn about the floor of the cave was pocketed with ant lion pits. Well, if the shelter was so clearly attractive to the hardy mountain cows, I reasoned, maybe in ancient times it was equally attractive to the ground sloths. I dug a test pit through the cow manure into sterile gravel and reached the floor of the cave without finding any ancient sloth dung or other fossils. Our guide had no information on *huesos fossiles* (fossil bones) from other caves. We started back, reaching Moris the next day, our skinny bestias somewhat energized now that they realized we were heading toward home.

Members of the party had business in Tucson, so we bid a fond good-bye to Gerardo, settled accounts with our guide and went out to the *pista de aterrizaje* (landing strip) to see what the Aeronca would do. Taking off in the heat of the afternoon when the air is thin and aircraft performance is compromised can be risky. After lumbering down the full length of the field, the Aeronca reluctantly lifted off and Ike began a slow circle low over the town, then low over the adjoining hills, skimming the foot of the mountains, gaining some speed while looking for extra lift in thermals. For half an hour we circled around Moris from one landmark, a peak on the east called the Sebastopol, toward a sugar loaf on the west, El Pilar, and back again, the altimeter slowly rising along with the engine temperature. At last, spotting some vultures spiraling up in a thermal above cliffs, Ike flew to join them. There was enough of an updraft to get us out of the hole, up over El Pilar, into cooler air, and on our way to spend the night in Hermosillo. *Gracias a dios y los zopilotes* (thanks to God and the vultures).

Back in Tucson Ike presented me with an itemized receipt (which I recently discovered in my 1960 field notes). My share of the expenses, including truck rental at Yecora, taxi and hotel at Hermosillo, hotel room and meals in Moris, guide service and rent of beasts, and customs fees and flying hours in the Aeronca, came to just $73.84! We all had a tremendous time. I had learned a few of the more common tropical trees and had begun to appreciate how good Gentry's plant information was, even in parts of the Río Mayo that he had not seen himself.

Recently I learned that the yellow or red outcrops may include altered or mineralized limonites known to geologists as gossans. No prospector seeking gold ignores them. I certainly did. No one can see what is not in his "search image." According to Thoreau, "We cannot see anything [even a scarlet oak in its brilliant fall colors, he said] until we are possessed with the idea of it, and then we can see hardly anything else" (*Journal,* November 4, 1858). A few years ago I drove back to Moris (there are roads everywhere now, including to and beyond Moris) with a geologist, Kik Moore, to find my friend, Gerardo, and to return with him to inspect his property outside the old mining settlement of Santa Maria. Next to Gerardo's gold mine were red and yellow altered rocks, plain as day, the hallmark of a promising mineralized district.

Eventually I forgot the wrecked Taylorcraft and my first dubious impression of Ike as a pilot. His knowledge of the Sierra was amazing, and the Sierra ranchers were devoted to him. We made many more trips together. So did many other border devotees from Tucson and elsewhere. We even flew the Aeronca across the Mexican Plateau (landing once by a Pemex station on the highway to refuel with car gas) and over cloud forest in the Sierra Madre Oriental to Xicotencatl in the cane fields carved out of the fast-vanishing tropical deciduous forest of the Tamaulipan coastal lowlands. Later, with his wife Jean, we flew in the Cessna through Egypt, the Sudan, East Africa, Mozambique and Madagascar. Another trip found us in South America east of the Andes in Tierra del Fuego before flying up the Amazon to Manaus, and northward into Venezuela by Angel Falls, with many stops along the way. Wonderful as they are, none of those other places seemed to have the irresistible wild charms of the Río Mayo country, with or without caves containing sloth dung!

January 1536: The Conquered Shamans

Over 450 years ago in the days of the conquistadors written history began in the Cajitan-speaking country these essays are about. The banks of the Yaqui River near modern Soyopa in Sonora was the scene of a strange tableau. Four travel-weary Spaniards (one of them actually an African slave), barefoot and threadbare, inspected a sign of deliverance. On the chest of an Indian was an amulet incorporating a horseshoe nail. After spending eight years in a strange foreign land, they were about to find their countrymen.

Followed by a large and faithful retinue of Indians, the four, led by Alvar Núñez Cabeza de Vaca, were venerated as shamans (witch doctors). They had known terrible times. Their journey began when Cabeza de Vaca, Alonso Castillo Maldonado, Andrés Dorantes, and Estevánico, a Moor from Morocco, alone survived the Pánfilo de Narváez expedition, which failed to find gold or to subdue Indians in Florida, rafted west past the Mississippi, and ended in shipwreck and in a cruel captivity on the Texas Coast. The captives hauled water and wood and tended night-long smudgy fires to protect their Han and Copoque masters from the attack of clouds of mosquitoes. The Spaniards were beaten with no provocation. They starved. Some resorted to cannibalism, the very abomination that Cortés and his army denounced when they found the Aztecs ceremonially practicing it in the Valley of Mexico. Ignorant of how to forage on the local plants and animals, the survivors found themselves contemptibly inferior to the natives at finding food.

Their Indian captors expected more from these exotic strangers. Against their better judgment but with no other alternative, the surviving castaways were eventually induced to attempt faith healing. To their own astonishment, the Spaniards discovered they had unexpected powers and were soon venerated as expert healers! Out of their unwilling "ordination" into shamanism they gained their freedom and began an incredible westward hegira of over one thousand miles to this spot on the Yaqui at 28.5° North, just upstream from the modern-day town of Onavas, on the threshold of the tropics. There they were detained by a winter flood.

Their unique odyssey through the interior of North America was no march of conquest, for they were thoroughly conquered and destitute. Along the way the Spaniards found themselves the vortex of a rolling potlatch, a continual flow of goods from tribe to tribe as each new people they encountered in turn gifted them royally in honor of their special powers. They, the beneficiaries, passed on the harvest to their previous guides and followers. Cabeza de Vaca's is one of the best accounts we have of an unknown America before enslaving, relocating or missionizing of natives, before the spread of distilled spirits, of the horse, of guns, and countless other introductions that forever shattered native societies. These Spaniards preceded the worst impact of the contact, long discounted or unrecognized, the outbreak of Old World diseases, especially smallpox, a lethal fifth column in the European invasion of America against which the natives had little resistance. Many tribes that Cabeza de Vaca's party encountered would not be heard of again.

When the Yaqui floods receded, the Spaniards crossed and sped south with their entourage, well inland from the Pacific Coast, on the back trail of their countrymen down through what is now Alamos and El Fuerte into the present-day State of Sinaloa. Geographer Carl Sauer called their route "the road to Cibola." It must have been in use prehistorically. Sinaloa lay in smoking ruins, its native inhabitants terrorized. Finally the long-hoped-for reunion between Cabeza de Vaca (in advance of the other castaways) and a band of Spanish cavalry took place. In shock, the Christian slavers viewed a sun-burned apparition speaking their tongue and surrounded by his native devotees. Troopers of the cruel captain, Nuño de Guzmán, learned that Cabeza de Vaca was second in command of the ill-fated Narváez expedition to Florida. Three hundred were lost and all others were believed dead.

After they had recovered themselves, the soldiers proceeded to instruct the Pimas (through an interpreter) to obey them as lords of the land. The four survivors (failed conquerors) were inconsequential, the Indians were told.

This in turn stunned the Pimas, whose home lay farther north and who were unitiated to the reality of conquest. They had seen and heard enough of the treatment of native Americans by these Christians not to want any part of it. They caucused among themselves and their verdict rings through the ages.

"The Christians lied: We [referring to Cabeza de Vaca and his companions] had come from the sunrise, they from the sunset; we healed the sick, they killed the sound; we came naked and barefoot, they clothed, horsed and lanced; we coveted nothing but gave whatever we were given, while they robbed whomever they found and bestowed nothing on anyone." The Indians held firm in their view. "To the last," Cabeza de Vaca reported, "I could not convince the Indians *that we were of the same people* as the Christian slavers [italics added]" *(Adventures in the Unknown Interior of America,* 128). No wonder. This time in the history of America contact meant more than conquest. The New World had conquered. In the wilderness between the Texas coast and the Sonoran foothills, four would-be conquistadors had their eyes and hearts opened. I think it trivializes matters to say they were "born again." They had discovered more about America than any of the other captains from Spain or Europe.

After several years of trying to improve a small course I once taught at the University of Arizona under the bloodless title of "environmental education," I discovered Cyclone Covey's translation of Cabeza de Vaca's report, a slender paperback titled *Adventures in the Unknown Interior of America.* The book would, I believed, help us avoid the all too common problem of selling the borderlands short and of making too much of Coronado's contribution to the exploration of the southwest.

Better yet, it provided an extra excuse, if one were needed, to promote a field trip into the Sonoran foothills, down to parallel 28.5° North, southeast of Hermosillo, into the Yaqui River country on the road to Cibola and to see the land Cabeza de Vaca first saw. There, near the inactive mines of La Barranca, we could begin to learn the tropical forest trees: guásima, palo chino, chilicote, torote and amapa, among a dozen others. I'd challenge the better hikers to find and investigate the plants present below and above the "cowline." The roughest upper part of Cerro Los Amoles (so named for its agaves, *Agave vilmoreana)* features slopes too steep to be ascended by mountain-bred *vacas* that are almost as sure-footed as goats.

On one trip Bill Gillespie and Diane Boyer censused the one hundred-foot-tall *sabinos* (Montezuma bald cypress) along the Arroyo San Xavier. On another, Kik Moore and Elliott Lax explored the curious natural barrens below green cliffs washed with copper salts and being mined for silver at Cerro Verde. On another, my truck broke down outside Tecoripa and the driver of a passing pickup, Manuel Duarte, stopped to offer help, a common courtesy in these parts. I accepted, and he towed me into his ranch for some shade-tree mechanical repairs. They worked wonders. Meanwhile, the students were enthusiastically exploring the Duarte ranch and had been invited in for coffee by Manuel's parents. An animated conversation in "borderlingua" (parts of Spanish and English) was in full swing.

Flowering amapa prieta and giant hecho cactus in the deciduous forest foothills.

Towering cliffs of the Sierra Alamos

Opposite: Tank bromeliads on rock canyon wall

A family living near the Río Cuchujaqui displays an ocelot pelt.

Opposite: Tangled roots of sabinos line the banks of the Río Cuchujaqui.

Campesino with buffel grass cut for cattle

Opposite: Hillsides bulldozed for buffel grass. Hecho cacti and kapok are the only forest remaining.

Cleared forest planted with buffel grass

At some point in our explorations someone would be sure to turn up an indigo snake, a boa constrictor, or an iguana-sized ctenosaur or perhaps spot one of the resident bald eagles hunting fish along the river. In camp above the Yaqui at the end of the day under the brightest of stars, we would cook a Dutch oven stew, keeping a sharp eye out for scorpions in the firewood. No trip ended without a baptismal dip in the river itself.

Here along the banks of the Yaqui there is much to ponder, like that business of rebirth. The year 2036 will soon arrive, five hundred years since a small group of Spaniards and their Indian followers passed this way on a magical journey. A suitable celebration would seem appropriate. It may not be too early to start preparing for it now. I envision a gathering of twenty-first–century shamans of various nationalities and ethnicities. They will be purged of excess baggage, skilled at sharing and healing without enslaving, and also skilled, as Cabeza de Vaca was, at something Chuck Bowden believes none of the rest of us have accomplished since.

Chuck calls it *living in America.*

March 1975: A Week Between the Ríos Yaqui and Mayo

The word spread through select parts of the campus and back up to the Desert Laboratory on Tumamoc Hill. Spring semester break would feature a special event for the tropical "honkies," border devotees, some even register-ing for course credit at the University of Arizona. We would cross the Sierra from Cuidad Obregón to Cuidad Chihuahua, a distance of some four hundred miles, most unpaved and the stretch from Yecora to Yepachic rarely traveled. We would sample habitats south of 28.5° North and west of 108° West, ending our ecological survey at the spectacular waterfall at the head of the Río Mayo, all of the trip in or near "Gentry Country." The recruits included ten University of Arizona students and five faculty members from three departments plus a geographer from the Boundary Commission at El Paso and a biology teacher from a California junior college. Finally, in Hermosillo, we were joined by Beatriz Braniff of the *Instituto Nacional de Antropología e Historia* (INAH). At the start of the trip she helped us find Rancho La Botana, an important Gentry locality outside Tesopaco, and she gave us a fine campfire talk on how the indigenous tribes, the Chichimecas of the border country, managed to elude foreign (European) conquest as long as they did.

Not everyone chose to go see La Botana, a Pleistocene deposit where Howard Gentry collected bones of Pleistocene mammoths and other extinct animals. The more ecologically minded members of the party wanted to lay hands on the dry tropical forest trees without delay. Joining Professor Will Van Asdall, they set up line transects in attractive patches of woods within easy reach of the road. Construction of a new paved road into the Sierra had barely begun, and we soon had to revert to the old road to Yecora via Santa Ana and Santa Rosa. Although narrow, slow, rough and often treacherous, it was evidently an improvement over the first road into Yecora via Bermudez as described by Pat Jenks. I appreciated once again the advantages of Sierra travel in a light plane.

At Tesopaco, a town of several hundred families, Beatriz Braniff consulted her list of contacts. She unearthed the name of a nurse, Alicia Clark de Gonzalez. How could there be a Sonoran with the surname of "Clark"? Almost surely Sra. Clark must be a descendant of the three Civil War soldiers whom various Sierra travelers, including Pat Jenks, have written about. Long ago three southerners left the States and ended up in the elbow of Chihuahua, leaving a large tribe of mostly blond-haired and blue-eyed mountaineers. In the cemetery at Bermudez their surnames, Clark, Moore and DeMoss, appear on most of the gravestones, and families with these names radiate out from Bermudez over the Mesa El Campanero, La Mesa Colorada, into the Sierra Obscura and down to La Mesa Atravesada.

Sra. Clark hunted down Juan Mateos, who turned out to be one of Gentry's original guides to La Botana. With Juan we had no trouble crossing some fences beyond the Tesopaco road through leafless woods illuminated by the pink flowers of the wild *jicama* vine *(Exogonium)* to find the grassy valley of La Botana. Geologist Geof Spaulding soon discovered a few bones weathering out, including a real prize, the diagnostic scales or scutes from the armored shell of an extinct glyptodont. Gentry had reported them from La Botana.

Glyptodonts were edentates, fossil relatives of the living tree sloths and giant anteaters, that looked more like giant armadillos. The largest full-grown glyptodont was not much smaller than a Volkswagen Beetle, armed in the rear with a clublike tail. Some glyptodont tails even ended in spikes like a mace. They ranged through South America, entering North America three million years ago when the Panamanian land bridge opened. Finding them at La Botana is of interest to paleontologists who thought glyptodonts might have been marsh or swamp dwellers. While open, the La Botana locality certainly is not marshy, at least not now. It is hill country covered with dry tropical forest.

Gentry also found fossils of *Taxodium,* the Montezuma bald cypress or sabino. The tree still grows along streams in the region; so perhaps the Sonora glyptodont lurked along the adjoining terrace. I envision them under attack by some large predator, for example, the large Pleistocene lion of the New World, akin to the African lion, which shared billing in America's extinct late Pleistocene game park. Too big to escape by digging holes like an armadillo, the glyptodont may have eluded its enemies by plunging into dense thorny *garabato* thickets, which it could safely penetrate because of its boney carapace. Rushing up in hot pursuit to tunnel in from behind, the would-be predator might suddenly find itself being clubbed over the head and ears by the glyptodont's heavy tail.

To be sure, my vision of how glyptodonts outwitted four-footed predators is fanciful. However, the likelihood that they and their edentate kin, the ground sloths, were totally vulnerable to the first human colonists of America requires no great imagination. Both would have been incredibly slow, easily tracked, and easily stoned or speared to death from a safe distance, even if sheltered inside a thorny tangle of garabato.

Furthermore, while we cannot be sure about the chronology, the time of glyptodont extinction being unknown in detail, the youngest radiocarbon dates on a relative, the extinct Shasta ground sloth, coincide remarkably with the first arrival of big-game hunters in the New World. Hence my interest in dry caves, where perishable remains of extinct animals may be found, including fossil remains that are ideal for the rigorous application of the radiocarbon dating method, which allows us to be considerably more precise about when large animals of the late Pleistocene disappeared than has been possible before.

What does any of this have to do with dry tropical forest and the cowboys who run their cattle in the Sierra? Under the moon around the campfire that night, some tongues were loosened by locally obtained distilled agave juice *(bacanora)*; opinions clashed. Supporters argued that the cattle were reasonable proxies for the extinct Ice Age megafauna and that the mountains were too rough and too dry to support many cows anyway. It might even be better for the plants to coexist with livestock than without them, especially those plants, like the *aguarito,* which rely on large mammals for seed dispersal. The antibovine faction objected to stepping in cow pies, to local terracing and erosion on steep slopes caused by many hooves, and to the threat of buffel grass invasion or other touted range "improvements," another manifestation of "bovine imperialism." Easy for us to say, we tourists from the north, the land of many imperialisms. The debate, I noticed, seemed to separate the plant transect people from the fossil hunters. Drowsily we went off to sleep to the whinnying hoots of elf owls calling at the edge of the dry tropical forest, some to dream the wild fantastic dreams to be expected when sleeping on the hard ground out of doors in an exotic land bathed in equinoctial moonlight. To be sure, few of our camps were so remote that we failed to detect a distant rooster crowing or ranch dog barking in the dawn.

The next day, a graduate student, Deborah Goldberg, unexpectedly came face to face with the subject of her dissertation, a geobotanical investigation she had not anticipated. We broke camp and drove deeper into the Sierra toward Santa Ana, totally unaware that we were coming upon the alleged locale of the famous lost treasure of Tayopa, much less that we were approaching what would become Deborah's study site, the place she would call "Vaca Valley." At the time none of us had read Frank Dobie's book, *Apache Gold and Yaqui Silver,* rich in stories of the route we were traveling and of buried treasure, especially of stories of Tayopa. Dobie came into this country in the opposite direction, from Chihuahua, riding horseback on the camino real after leaving the railroad at Miñaca. He was looking for silver; we were looking for plants.

An enthusiastic ecologist, Deborah was not aware of lost mines of the Jesuits or tales of buried silver around Tayopa, "the richest mine of all." What caught her eye were the red barren hills; "red *topueste* dirt" Dobie called it from his treasure map, the type of habitat that I had overlooked outside Moris fifteen years earlier, the altered soil of a mining district.

All field ecologists familiar with the border region "know" that at their lower limits oaks and pines are restricted to cool, moist sites. Here at an elevation just over two thousand feet outside Santa Ana, we were enveloped by a dry tropical forest of *mauto, palo santo, pochote* and *tepeguaje.* At higher elevations we fully expected to (and would) see this habitat give way to oak woodland and eventually to pine-oak woodland and forest, the oaks and pines appearing first in cool, moist ravines and then on north slopes.

But right here, outside Santa Ana near Dobie's Guadalupe de Tayopa, that wasn't the way it was. When we *first saw* many oaks (and later the pines), they were *not* confined to north slopes or most ravines. We were driving east toward the settlement of Santa Ana on the side of a ridge that sloped *south.* The ridge included patches of Dobie's red topueste soils, and that was where the oaks grew, no matter whether the slopes faced south, west, east or north, in any direction as long as there were outcrops of red soils. Each patch of the altered red soils supported oaks or hop bush, and apparently not much else. The gray soils surrounding the red patches were clothed with low, dense dry tropical forest, making an impressive mosaic. By not being dependent on wet ravines or cool north slopes, the oaks were thumbing their noses, so to speak, at the ecological rules. That was enough to capture Deborah's interest and to bring her back on many more trips to Santa Ana.

She stopped the vans and recruited volunteers to take line transects inside and outside the oak communities. She suspected, and later determined, that the red soils were highly acidic; they have a pH (the measure of acidity or alkalinity) of 4.5 or less. The acidity interferes with nutrient transport. Normal soils in the region are less acidic. We were in a region of rhyolites and welded tuff, capped by basalt mesas outside Yecora. The red spots apparently were formed by the extreme temperatures and pressures associated with past volcanic activity; the acidity, by sulfides released in the process. On the red soils the oaks (and at a slightly higher elevation, egg cone pines) could escape competition with trees of the dry tropical forest. Later, Deborah's experiments showed that the oaks can tolerate the acidity better than other trees of the region. Beyond guiding the prospector in a search for precious metals, Deborah showed that the red topueste dirt can guide the philosophical investigator to discoveries about community composition and plant competition under extreme conditions.

Finishing a preliminary survey of the oak habitat, we proceeded on to Santa Ana where we saw our first *güérigo,* the handsome white cottonwood *(Populus monticola)* limited to the foothills and valleys of eastern Sonora. Frank Dobie mentions it as a botanical clue for treasure hunters in search of Tayopa. As Dobie discovered, the güérigos are local; they go no further south, not even entering the Sierra Obscura in the Río Mayo country. The cottonwood for which Alamos is named and the tree along the lower Río Mayo is a different species, *Populus mexicana.* Neither grow naturally in Arizona, although both are planted on the University of Arizona campus.

The one acquisition we made in Santa Ana was not Jesuit silver but cuts of a freshly butchered beef, steaks and liver, the steaks much too fresh, it turned out, when we tried to cook them in camp that night. Unhung mountain grown beef can be too tough even for mountain grown appetites!

Beyond Santa Ana the last topueste outcrops seen along the road to Yecora are associated with mines at Santa Rosa and La Trinidad. There, at three to four thousand feet in elevation, the "soup bowl oak" *(Quercus pennivenia)* whose leaf is the shape of a soup bowl also defies botanical life zone rules by reaching its lower limit with no regard for aspect, thanks to the acidic red soils.

We entered Yecora the next day. I noticed few changes from what I remembered of it from my flight with Ike. To be sure, instead of fifty-gallon drums one could now buy gasoline out of a pump. While filling up, we were suddenly and unexpectedly assailed by young men in masks, gaudy costumes, and squeaky voices, the *fariseos* (pharisees) of Lent whose high jinks included brazen fund-raising techniques that stripped us of pocket change! It was all for the benefit of the church, said geography professor Dave Bradbury. At Yecora we also heard of the fate of Dave Cauginaugh, one of the best Sierra pilots. I had met him in Hermosillo through Ike Russell after our Moris trip. Ike claimed that he learned many tricks of mountain piloting from Dave. No trick in Dave's book could help him when the end came. Flying through the mountains, Dave had suffered a heart attack and had gone down with his three passengers; none survived. We would camp that night on his airstrip outside his ranch at El Trigo, near a mountain stream lined with alders and said to harbor otters.

By Easter Saturday we had been driving for days in our lowest gears over rough mountain roads that were steadily getting worse. The higher we climbed, the colder the nights became. In our valley camps, along sparkling streams lined with somber evergreen *tascate (Cupressus)* trees, we suffered the effects of cold-air drainage. At dawn it was very hard to leave warm sleeping bags to enter an icy world white with hoar frost. Finally we reached the Pima settlement of Maicoba, only to be "held up" by more wildly enthusiastic fariseos, who never expected so many gringos. At noon we were well into Chihuahua, up in the extreme northeastern corner of Gentry's Río Mayo region, pressed for time and thinking of home.

Looking for gas, we left our route and entered the town of Yepachic pushing through packed throngs of Sierra people, far more than we had expected and, obviously, far more than the town itself would normally shelter. An Easter crowd, assembled from all over the Sierra, was streaming around the churchyard where we found an amazing scene.

Up on the roof of the church, above wreaths of desert spoon *(Dasilyrion)*, one man vigorously pounded a drum while another swung an ear-splitting wooden ratchet. A crush of people watched men run in and out of the church. The men began wrestling, each trying to throw over his opponent by pulling him up by the waist. Paul Fugate and other sturdy types in our group declined kind invitations to join in. The local rites of spring were new to most of us. Finally some hardy native playing the part of Judas (so identified by Dave Bradbury) was pounced on by the churchyard mob, which proceeded to raise him up and carry him bodily over their heads to throw him over the wall, where he was caught in mid air by the assembly outside the churchyard and tossed back in.

Much relieved that none of us had been recruited to understudy Judas, we made a few purchases at the store, which lacked gasoline, and escaped, we thought, to resume our journey on the lumber-truck road deeper into the Sierra toward fuel and pavement at the big lumber mill at Tomochic. The final goal, the ultimate highlight of the survey, was supposed to be a side trip to the waterfall at Basaseachic. We were already a day late.

Nevertheless, we did not escape so easily. A few miles out of Yepachic an obviously distressed and agitated native rushed out of his cabin to intercept us. Bravely he dragged a large pine log across the road in front of the first of five truck loads of heathen gringos. It seemed that, on this holy day, no one was supposed to travel. In retrospect, he was right. It was rash and thoughtless of us to leave Judas to his fate back there. Others in the party were having second thoughts about turning down invitations to the Saturday night dance. Should we stay for the rest of the Pascua festivities? On Bradbury's suggestion, a modest contribution, fifty pesos, was offered to the Indian enforcer of tradition. This seemed to soften his attitude toward us, and kindly he removed the barrier. We were again on the road to the water-fall.

Outside Tomochic on Easter Sunday morning, at an elevation of sixty-six hundred feet, our camp by the side of the road was intensely cold, much too cold for those who were tentless in light sleeping bags intended for camping in the tropical lowlands. Going to Basaseachic would take the entire day. All the trucks were low on gas. A split developed. Some simply had to meet university classes to give or take quizzes in Tucson on Monday. Others felt they had equally demanding responsibilities at home. We had been warned that one week is too little for both crossing and investigating the Sierra. How we all yearned for a few extra "idle days." To the dismay of his students, Professor Ron Pulliam left with grim determination. After driving a few miles with the "gotta-go-home" group he changed his mind and returned to rejoin the waterfall detachment, to cheers and whistles of the truants.

The extra effort was rewarded. Apart from its scenic splendor, the Basaseachic waterfall is a botanical oasis very rich in endemic species, al-though most would not flower until late summer or fall. Much warmer than where we had camped, the base of the falls supported scarlet salvia, purple lupines, *Lobelia,* rare sedges and many other colorful early spring plants. A Tarahumara Indian, climbing the steep trail beside the waterfall, held a string of native trout, one of which was reluctantly sold to us for a scientific speci-men after considerable bargaining. The species, *Salmo chrysogaster,* was first described only ten years earlier and had not been recorded before from the Río Mayo drainage.

The height of the fall has been measured by geographer Bob Schmidt of the University of Texas at El Paso. He used a fishing pole and reel, with a sinker on his line. The drop, almost straight down, is eight hundred and thirty feet. In the dry season, the time of our visit, a small stream cascades into a wispy spray. In the rainy season it is a thunderous torrent. In the gorge, big-toothed maples and basswood were coming into new leaf, war-blers were starting to migrate, and the moist woods felt lush and nurturing like an Appalachian cove forest in spring. The trees included holly, hop hornbeam, silk tassel, tascate (Arizona cypress) and at least ten species of oaks. With mixed emotions we learned of plans for a new tourist hotel to be connected by a paved road from Cuidad Chihuahua and to Cuidad Obregón. The pavement is now complete and in a day tourists comfortably drive across the Sierra over the route we had slowly bounced along for almost a week. When they get to Basaseachic, I hope some take the trouble to hike down below the falls to see the wonderful tascate woods and ten species of oaks.

Make no mistake, I am told by some of the most venturesome university students that wild country is still left; it starts below the waterfall at Basaseachic and heads south and west for one hundred miles into Sonora, a roadless maze of mountain trails above a wild river known only to the *gente de la Sierra* (mountain folks). It is the country I once peered into from the Mesa La Polvosa.

We clambered back up to our trucks and had to resort to draining the white gas from our stoves to squeeze out enough fuel to reach Tomochic. It was well after midnight Tuesday morning when the last vehicles reached Tucson. In some cases, home would never again be quite the same and certain members of the spring Sierra trip of 1975 would discover reasons to return or to go on deeper into Mexico. The borderlands can do that.

March 1990: The Buffel Grass Bomb

Merv Larson knows all the roads around Alamos. He kept insisting there was a new one, a lumber road east out of Alamos up into the pines at Santa Barbara. Back in the 1950s a rough lumber-truck road led up the Cuchujaqui valley into the Sierra at Milpillas. Then, many years ago, above Rancho Los Amoles the rains washed it out. To be sure, at Los Amoles the road ends in beautiful mountain country within the lower range of the *barba de chivato (Calliandra houstoniana),* a handsome shrub whose long rose-purple anthers dry into a brown "goat's beard." Barba de chivato promises to become an outstanding ornamental for the border region. Nevertheless, Rancho Los Amoles itself is just below the elevation of the lumber-mill country. I wanted to explore the new road and see the effect of the fresh cutting, before more damage was done.

Merv guaranteed both cut and uncut pines. So a spring break trip, with a group of students and friends, that began on the Mesa El Campanero outside Yecora ended at Merv's in Alamos. He is restoring the old hospital on the southeast side of town.

Merv has transplanted many of the dry-forest trees into a giant planter, like a megawindow box, in front of his *portal.* He waters them, and his night watchman, Teodoro, a retired Alamos cop, poisons the *mochomos* (leaf cutter ants, *Atta)* before they can strip the foliage. There are *torotes* of various kinds (native *Bursera, Fouquieria* and *Jatropha), palo santo, guajilote (Bombax),* a giant *tempisque (Sideroxylon),* which fruits in June, and *ensangregado (Jatropha platanifolia),* a much larger and more robust version of limber bush than the one that grows in the Sonoran Desert around Tucson.

Many tropical forest trees are shallowly rooted and can be transplanted with ease. One problem is that, even if one wages war on the ants and provides good soil and water, some of the dry-forest trees are stubbornly deciduous. No matter how wet the winter or spring may be, they will not leaf out until shortly before the summer rains are due in late June (San Juan's Day according to tradition). And, despite ample moisture supplied by Merv's hose, some insist on defoliating as early as September. Phenologically the trees know what they are doing. Unless adapted to moist soils in a floodplain habitat, they cannot rely on fall to be wet enough to sustain photosynthesis. Sonora is not Veracruz! Merv's plantation of natives is an excellent place to start learning the trees and the behavior of dry tropical forest. Even when leafless, the torotes, palo santo and other trees of the region are graceful and their trunks are quite distinct. One must admire the adaptation the trees have to the short summer rainy season, only ten to fifteen weeks, the one time in the year when all trees are in full leaf.

Friday morning we rounded up friends from various corners of Alamos, including Chuck Bowden and Stephanie Meyer, an Alamos ecologist, and started out for the pines. On the way, Merv promised, we would see *guajilote (Bombax palmeri),* a tropical tree in the baobab family, Bombacaceae. As we climbed out of the Cuchujaqui valley we came upon them, their large white blossoms wilting in the sun on the tips of naked, spreading, leafless branches. Their nocturnal flowering and wide-spaced, wide-open branches afford uncluttered access to sturdy white flowers with numerous long stamens (shaving brush tree), suggesting chiropterophily, the bat pollination syndrome. That does not mean that only bats can pollinate guajilote, but lots of their pollen has been found in guts of certain tropical bats such as the long-nosed bat, *Leptonycteris.* If bees visit the flowers, they will not easily intercept the stamens, which extend several inches above the nectar.

A good field trip discovers the unexpected. While George Ferguson climbed up into the *Bombax* to photograph flowers at close range, another student, Juan Rascon, struck up a conversation with a campesino working nearby. There was a fine tract of dry tropical forest above us. The man was clearing some of it. Juan asked why.

"To plant maize, señor."

"Is it your land?" Juan asked.

"No, señor, the owner lives in Navojoa. He pays me 300,000 pesos [about $100] a hectare [three acres] to cut down the monte. Then I will plant maize."

"And what does he get out of it?" Juan persisted.

"After my corn crop, when the field will no longer produce, he will plant buffel [*Pennisetum ciliare,* the South African perennial grass widely introduced into Sonora starting in the 1970s]. He will fence it for his cattle." Juan also learned that the new owners from cities on Highway 15 may care little for the people of the Sierra, in some cases fencing the gente off the land, employing outsiders, and leaving the locals with no source of income or even subsistence.

All this was sobering news for us to mull over around the campfire that night. Buffel is a favorite solution of range managers seeking to improve production in the dry tropical forest. Woods that yield sparse forage and make cattle roundups *muy trabajoso* (hard work) for cowboys, who must search hard in the dense monte for their elusive stock, are much easier to manage when converted *(desmontar)* into open buffel grass pastures. The wily Criollo cattle of the forest are replaced by lazy Charolais cattle of the pastures.

Most tourists driving from Navojoa to Alamos will not realize the damage already done over the last twenty years. West of the Cerro Prieto and along the road to Mocuzari Dam, vast tracts of forest have been cut down by hand or, increasingly, smashed down by bulldozer, the trunks burned after they dry out and the ruins turned into buffel grass pastures. The place now looks like an African savanna with cattle standing belly high in buffel grass. Tourists and other visitors may prefer the openness to the claustrophobic feeling enveloping a narrow road enclosed by dense and mysterious woods, possibly the haunts of desperados. Indeed, if local people are dispossessed by new owners, there will be more landless peasants for the *mafiosos* (drug lords) to recruit as growers of marijuana and opium poppies. There will be more unrest in the monte, which has already seen its share of murders.

Given half a chance, the dry forest trees recover if their stumps are not bulldozed. In mature dry tropical forest Howard Gentry reported thirty-three to forty-five species of trees and shrubs in half an acre. Four years after the abandonment of a corn field in hand-cleared forest (Sonorans call these fields *rozas*), Gentry found twenty species of trees, one up to ten feet tall, some sprouting from stumps. Twelve to twenty years after clearing, there were twenty-five woody species; the pochote were twenty-five feet tall. Recovery was well underway. The cycle is slow but renewable, and eventually the forest can be cut again and in the ashes another maize crop can be harvested. With modifications, this is the classic land-use pattern of subsistence adopted by campesinos growing corn in *milpas* (cornfields) in much of rural Mexico. The system depends on forest recovery, which in the Sonora-Chihuahua border country is slow but sure. Hand-clearing of rozas or milpas by subsistence farmers is not permanently damaging to the forest.

In contrast, the new buffel grass pastures don't give the trees a chance to recover. The dense grass prevents germination or seedling establishment. While ranchers often leave "keeper trees," large *palo santo, palo blanco, mauto,* thirty-foot-tall, mature columnar cacti called *hechos, palo cachora* and others to provide shade, edible fruit, or fence posts, these trees are doomed. If not cut down first, the keeper trees will die of old age or be blown down in storms, leaving the field exclusively to the buffel grass. For the buffel to remain thrifty, it must be grazed heavily or burned. Meanwhile more and more dry tropical forest and thorn forest is being destroyed for buffel grass. Based on what we saw, we guessed that already about half of the natural forest on rolling country along the upper Río Cuchujaqui has been sacrificed. Steeper mountainsides further away from the river resist mechanical destruction by bulldozers and may be cleared by hand, as we witnessed on the road to Santa Barbara.

Fortunately, there still is much to save. Stephanie Meyer has supported the idea of preserving the Sierra de Alamos, a concept initiated by foresters of *Secretaria de Agricultura y Recursos Hidraulicos* (SARH) and endorsed by the municipality of Alamos. The Sierra de Alamos, looming over the town of the same name, is thoroughly isolated from the rest of the Sierra Madre and is the home of many interesting tropical plants and animals at or near their northern limit. At the foot are excellent examples of uncut or selectively cut dry tropical forest. On top are pines, oaks and exposed cliffs supporting tank bromeliads and epiphytic orchids. Most of the area is too steep for cultivation or grazing; it is the main watershed for Alamos, not to mention a magnificent scenic backdrop for the town. We could survey it from the road to Santa Barbara. Over ninety percent is uncleared.

A man coming down from Santa Barbara, Ruben Alvarez, assured us that the steep climb ahead was passable for four-wheel-drive vehicles. We drove past a small cave, the roost of fig-eating bats, admired great golden blossoms on a *palo barril (Cochleosperma)* and emerged on a mesa of yellow volcanic tuff with stunted Chihuahua oaks and a very attractive sunflower bush, *Tithonia,* that looked like a great prospect for gardeners. Spring annuals including a pink-purple gentian, annual grasses and tiny sedges were scattered about.

Higher still we came to blue oaks festooned with epiphytes including the green cigar-shaped pseudobulbs of *Laelia,* a sturdy tree orchid whose large lilac flowers appear in October. We found Santa Barbara in a beautiful valley at four thousand feet surrounded by forest and supporting well-made scattered ranch houses, all occupied by heirs or relatives of Don Chico, the senior member of the Alvarez clan. In July, we learned, oxen plow the new bean fields. Chuck and Merv returned to town; the rest of us found a camp site in the pines below a red peak with tank bromeliads, Cerro Agujudo.

The Alvarez boys came over to visit our camp, hospitably offering to share a bottle of *lechuguilla,* a local mescal distilled from the cow horn agave. After exchanging pleasantries, they eventually inquired about what we were up to. "We are looking for unusual trees and shrubs native to the Sierra."

"Well, if that's what you want, you should have a look at Arroyo Verde. There are lots of strange plants there," they replied.

"Arroyo Verde? Where is that?"

"Just below your camp," said Beto Alvarez, "down in this canyon. Do you know about the stinging bush, the *ortiguilla?* In summer there is so much ortiguilla no one goes into the Arroyo Verde, not even the cattle."

We knew about *mala mujer* (bad woman), a stinging plant of summertime in southern Arizona, occasionally found in southern Sonora. We did not know ortiguilla *(Urera),* which, according to Gentry, was the name for a stinging shrub found along mountain streams.

The canyon dropped away precipitously below us. Down there was Arroyo Verde, too remote to explore in the half day we had left for fieldwork before leaving for a swim in the Gulf at Huatabampito. Arroyo Verde sounded very inviting, and plans were soon hatched to return to explore it in May after the semester ended. The main discovery for us on this trip was not the uncut pine woods of Santa Barbara. It was the conversation Juan Rascon had with the man cutting down the monte for buffel grass. We had discovered the buffel grass bomb.

May 1991: The Forest Nobody Knows

To make up for a lack of appreciation in New England at the time, Henry David Thoreau wrote an essay, "Autumnal Tints." It dwelt on the glorious fall colors of sugar maples, scarlet oaks and other trees of the eastern deciduous forest, a phenomenon unknown in Europe, unanticipated by European colonists, and invisible to many New England farmers in Thoreau's time.

The dry tropical forest along the foot of the Sierra is much less well known, even now, than the New England forests were in Thoreau's day. Dry tropical forest is wetter and taller than thorn forest of the southern Sonoran coastal plain and drier and shorter than New England woods. All are deciduous in their own way, losing leaves either to frost or to drought. Dry tropical forest extends to 29° North with occasional species even beyond, a narrow finger pointing up out of the tropics almost touching the Sonora-Arizona border. When Alberto Burquez, a young Sonoran ecologist raised in Hermosillo and familiar with the Sonoran Desert from his childhood, went as a teenager to Alamos, the trees looked so big and handsome that he thought he was seeing a tropical jungle. He grew up in a place where no native upland trees exceeded twelve feet in height; a canopy twenty to forty feet above the ground was indeed impressive.

From the main plaza in Alamos one can sip a cool drink and gaze into second growth dry tropical forest covering steep hills at the edge of town less than a mile away. Here, in Sonora, the trees may not be huge (although some figs are), but they still make up fine woods, as the young Alberto Burquez realized. Hot climates, typically innocent of frost or snow, appropriately dry most of the year and predictably wet at least two months in summer, are what this forest needs.

Alberto and his wife, Angelina ("Gela" to her friends) Martínez, recently earned doctorates in biology at Cambridge University in England. They are part of the new cadre of enthusiastic and highly skilled Mexican ecologists investigating their homeland. Mexico is extraordinarily rich in plants and animals, especially along the interface of the temperate and tropical forests that twist and turn endlessly through mountains and barrancas of the Sierra Madre, the sort of tropical maze I was looking into from Mesa La Polvosa in 1956.

We (Gela, Alberto, their two small boys, Berti and Emilio, botanist Phil Jenkins from Tucson and I) had gathered on Stephanie Meyer's cool portal outside Alamos next to the airport. With the cooperation of a neighbor, an Alaskan bush pilot in his other life, Stephanie had arranged a flight for us up the Cuchujaqui. Gela brought her video camera, and for almost an hour as we flew low above the river she taped the dry tropical forest and the encroaching new pastures, some scarred by piles of freshly burned trees left by ranchers preparing *lebensraum* for buffel grass. How I wished I had video tapes from my earlier flights! Gela and Alberto were well acquainted with the trees, the habitat and the threats to it through their own research at Chamela, a field station operated in Jalisco by Mexico's Instituto de Biologia of the *Universidad Nacional Autonoma de Mexico,* better known as UNAM. Chamela is some 450 miles south of southern Sonora. Just as New Englanders can trace their forest trees—beech, sugar maple, red oak, hemlock, hickory—into rich, moist woods as far south as South Carolina or Georgia, so the trees of the dry forest around Alamos (locally called *monte mohino)* can be traced far to the south through seasonally dry parts of southern Mexico into dry interior valleys in Central America.

Although far less brilliant than in New England's fall, the Sonoran trees also display changing colors in their foliage. In September and October the hills are golden as the torotes turn yellow. In winter the leaves of *palo colorado* and *basil* glow russet red. Far more impressive are the flowers that completely outdo those of temperate forest trees. Tropical trees store energy in summer and budget appropriately for flowering in the dry season when bird, bat and insect pollinators can more easily penetrate the bare leafless branches. Unlike the conifer or hardwood forests of North America, in which the majority of the trees are wind pollinated (to the distress of allergics), the forests of the tropics, those around Alamos included, are almost exclusively animal pollinated. That means the trees produce attractive flowers or copious nectar and pollen, a veritable feeding station, for suitable animal pollinators. Flowering can vary according to annual rainfall. Flowering in the spring of 1991 was especially intense after a very wet winter and preceding summer.

Back at her house that night Stephanie Meyer showed us slides, taken in her two years at Alamos, that captured the changing seasons. Starting in November, the spectacular morning-glory trees are tipped with white blossoms that look like ping-pong balls, "white corollas like stars against the morning sky," Howard S. Gentry wrote. "These stars soon fall upon the ground where the deer eat them." In January the amapas, valued as timber trees, are in full bloom, a haunting rose-red color on otherwise naked branches of the dark-trunked trees on the hills, softly glowing in the mild winter sun. In the understory during early spring, a shrubby cassia is covered with bright yellow flowers, its pollen released only by small native bees known as buzz pollinators. Their wings must vibrate at the proper frequency to shake out the pollen. The large purple flowers of a roadside nightshade, *sacamanteca,* also require buzz pollinators. In March abundant large blossoms, suggesting golden torches, mark the position of each *palo barril,* a stately tree of the upper slopes. Red accent appears in April, thanks to blossoms covering the *torote verde* or tree ocotillo, a relative of the coachwhip of Arizona and the borderlands. May brings large creamy white flowers on guajilote, while in May and June the incessant blue of guayacán and nesco is punctuated by red trumpets of the chilicote, a tubular flower sought by hummingbirds. In late summer and fall there is a blanket of color from a sulfur-orange cosmos (now popular as a garden flower) along with purple bells on morning-glory vines and fox-glovelike flowers on the *aguarcito,* whose flat-lying upper leaves close to clasp prayerfully at night. November comes and the tree morning-glories begin again. Any one of these and other breathtaking botanical outbursts that I have not mentioned would be sufficient to justify a major pilgrimage, like the gathering in May of hundreds of thousands of Philadelphia suburbanites driving through Valley Forge, Pennsylvania, to see dogwood in bloom. There is much celebrating to do if all the "botanical birthdays" of Alamos are to be acknowledged. Along with the saints's days on the calendar, we need individually named weeks or months to commemorate the expected sequential flowering of the trees, shrubs and vines of this neglected tropical world.

Fruits and fruiting are also budgeted by each species. On the hillsides some trees *(vara prieta* and *palo colorado)* throw their seeds through the air with a sudden twist of the drying pod. Others endow their seeds with a feathery parachute, especially noticeable in the big white powder puffs of kapok *(Ceiba)* fruits, which hang on the trees through the winter. In the lowlands mesquite, *guamúchil, guinora* (boat spine acacia), strangling figs, tropical hackberry and other trees that grow along fence rows or near streams, the natural haunts of mammals and birds, have fruits designed to attract hungry mammals and birds. It would seem that the fruits expect to be taken to their favorite habitat by their animal vectors. The cascade of sugary pulp investing the pods of mesquite and *guinolo,* dropped in June at the end of a long dry season, is eagerly sought by large herbivores. After gorging, they defecate the undamaged seeds in a spot the animal picks, often shady, on soft ground and near water, at a point some distance away from the parent tree, in similar habitat, just what the mesquite or other tasty fruited tree had "intended" for its progeny in the first place.

Above the floodplains, the stony hills of southern Sonora are clothed in thorn forest or dry tropical forest. They rarely support mesquite or similar trees with sugary fruits. When they do, the exceptions usually grow along a trail crossing a low pass or saddle that is favored by livestock in hot weather, the kind of place animals will seek for cool breezes and to escape bugs, along the easiest path. Their manure accumulates, including mesquite seeds from pods the animals ate down below. The result is to establish a few extralocal mesquite trees up on the airy *puertos* (passes across hills).

The sweet pods of mesquite have a long history. They did not evolve in response to cattle or horses or other domestic newcomers, ourselves included. Presumably, the extinct megafauna I have alluded to earlier, the native American elephants, extinct horses, ground sloths and glyptodonts, were the intended dispersers for the fallen fruit. The tasty wild fruits designed to entice mammals and birds was part of the Garden of Eden gift to our species. After the megafaunal extinctions, beans of mesquite and other legumes, fruits of *guaiparín* (Sonoran persimmon) and other fruiting trees helped sustain native Americans in the Sonoran region. People and their livestock are now the proxies for the extinct beasts, helping to disperse the native trees.

The destiny of this land and its natives is being shaped by many forces and the outcome is unclear. There is a major opportunity now for those who love the Sierra, the montane oaks, pines and especially the many tropical species in the dry tropical forest of the foothills and barrancas to join forces.

Sonorans and Chihuahuans and their supporters outside the region have a chance to discover and secure values that are easily crushed by narrow economic determinism. The problem of value, of wildness versus development, haunts our generation, this century, our world. If a modest economic return is possible when *vaqueros* (cowboys) run Corriente cattle in the woods rather than Charolais cattle in cleared pastures, is that enough to save both the monte, the Corriente stock and the life style of vaqueros themselves? Are there *gente de visión* to step forward and explore ways to help preserve the Sierra de Alamos and the "Forests of the Night," the wild country above a wild river, the Río Mayo rushing down from its birthplace beyond Moris to San Bernardo, through the land of the Warihio, the deer, and the jaguar?

Chuck Bowden and Jack Dykinga, Alberto Burquez and Stephanie Meyer and others are optimistic. Mexican governmental agencies SARH and the *Secretaría de Desarroyo Urbano y Ecología* (SEDUE) are planning an ecological preserve for the Sierra de Alamos. The new *Centro Ecologico de Sonora* and the even newer branch of the *Centro de Ecologia,* UNAM, in Hermosillo, along with politicians and range managers are exploring conservation initiatives. The monte east of Highway 15 is no longer an unknown world. Of course, it never was unknown to its real denizens, the people of the Sierra, who shared some of its secrets with Howard Gentry and are eager to share more with a new generation.

The country people have a word for a beloved place, derived from the Spanish verb *querer,* to love or to want. The Sierra is their *querencia,* their heartland. One must admire their feelings and their insight. The querencias of this land cry for appreciation, protection and a new vision of stewardship.

*Woman weaving
sleeping mats in the
Sierra Alamos village of
Aguas Calientes.*

Flowering nesco

Opposite: Flowering Bombax

Above: The rainy season
Opposite: The dry season at exactly the same
location.

43

Organ-pipe cactus with Queen's Wreath

Opposite: Sabino with tangled roots on the bank of the Río Cuchujaqui.

Overleaf: Ficus growing in cliff bank on the Río Cuchujaqui.

The Secret Forest

Entrada

ALL TALES IN THIS HEMISPHERE BEGIN as a collision between worlds. We are only human and, being human and creatures of the flesh, we create stories and fables about how we came to this place and what we found. We tell of murderous conquistadors, of filthy savages, of saintly priests, of whip-wielding padres, of barren, harsh ground, of the mission of civilization.

We live many different forms of consciousness. We are a perpetual virgin that calls itself the New World. We are the energy and might of Europe that calls itself Progress. We are slaves shuffling off stinking hulks in a hundred harbors, our shackles clanging and our tongues denied a voice. We are native races that can barely recall our beginnings and we will not concede that we will cease to hold this ground. We are of many colors. We are of many nations but we are of one biology.

Our records are scant, largely one sided, and drenched in blood and spirit. But even given all the beliefs that crowd our heads and blind our eyes, sometimes our earliest impressions have a power that centuries cannot still:

These Indians ever stayed with us until they safely delivered us to others. They were all convinced that we came from Heaven.

> Alvar Núñez Cabeza de Vaca in Sonora, from his *Adventures in the Unknown Interior of America*, trans. and ed. Cyclone Covey (1963; reprinted Albuquerque: University of New Mexico Press, 1983), 120.

Those who went ahead returned to tell us that there were warriors waiting for us ahead. So we gathered our things and, dividing ourselves into a vanguard and a rear guard, marched towards the Indian warriors, who were assembling in a large field of one-and-a-half leagues. When they saw us, they began to march towards us very boldly, throwing fistfuls of dirt into the air, flexing their bows and making fierce grimaces . . . . An old man more distinguished than the others, because he wore a black robe like a scapulary, studded with pearls, and surrounded by dogs, birds and deer and many other things. And as it was morning, and the sunlight fell on him, he blazed like silver. He carried his bow and arrows, and a wooden staff with a very elaborate handle, and was in control of the people.

> Anonymous Reporter in Sonora, 1533, in Evelyn Hu-DeHart, *Missionaries, Miners & Indians* (Tucson: University of Arizona Press, 1981), 14.

We can bury our past but not escape its bony hands upon our shoulders. Just as we can deny the natural world but never survive without it—not our bodies, not our minds, not our souls. We are all fools but this can be a blessing. We simply must admit to being fools and then, we can begin to act with the caution, and the kindness and the love that is denied those who know things absolutely.

I am a fool and I was fortunate enough to find a place that gently taught me this fact.

❖

The woman puts a venison stew before me on a chipped old plate; one of the men cracks the top off a beer as the night seeps off the mountain into the village. A naked light bulb dangles over my head under the ramada and everyone is smiling. It has been a bad year. The rains have been treacherous. First they were late and the men had to wait to plant the corn in their milpas. Then, when the storms finally came they dropped scant moisture. Finally, in August, when the stalks had struggled against the sun and were beginning to form tiny ears, the storms returned with a strong heart, the skies drained down onto the land, the dry arroyos filled and the water spilled out of the banks, and the corn, the sacred corn, began to rot in the fields. Ah, the corn, it is easy to think of it this night as the woman, Ramona, the mother of so many, who puts a plate of fresh tortillas before me. She has ground the kernels on her stone metate, patted the wafers out by hand, cooked them over a wood fire. She is very good at this, but who would not be after say forty years of rising at 3:30 in the morning to prepare them for the men going to the fields and the forest.

Everyone is happy tonight. I can hear the pig snuffling about at the edge of the group, hoping for slops. I can see the thin dogs out of the corner of my eye, skulking behind the legs of the men clumped in circles of soft conversations in the swept dirt yard. Minerva is seventeen tonight and she is in full bloom. What do I know of her? She came to my house in town once to use the shower before a big dance. She came to my house once with a cactus thorn in her eye and I drove her thirty miles to a doctor. She always smiles and radiates an appetite for life that thrills boys and spooks her guardians. That is what I know. Her uncles, five of whom still live in the house, pool their money so that she can go to dances and meet a man who will take her away and feed her. They tell me this matter-of-factly. Everything here is matter-of-fact and all the facts sound like fantasy. The forest is the world of the uncles and they speak of water demons, birds they call *carbuncos* who beam blue lights from their heads, dogs who live in the water, trees that bear strange fruit, an old woman who lives with military macaws, a giant snake that camps on the edge of the village. They talk of killings, of births, of loves, of feuds. That is why I am here, an accidental captive in their net. And the net is simply life. For tonight, I have brought a lacy tube top for Minerva as a gift, a wrapping to help her in her hunts at the dances. This article has made her mother Ramona very happy. I think she will pray for me.

It all started much more simply and dully. I was that investigator of an ecosystem—my God, how the word used to trip from my tongue. I had a chance to visit an old place and this time to come into a country with new eyes. I had a chance to go, to stop moving about and finally sink into some ground. The brute geography is very straight forward: Tropical Sonora begins about two hundred miles south of the American border with the best point of entry four hundred miles south of the line at the small city of Alamos. This tongue of tropical vegetation is the northern limit of a biological world that stretches far south into the narrows of Central America and the closest place for a visit by residents of the United States. Here the parrots, the military macaws and the occasional jaguar can be found.

This ground hosts the most threatened type of tropical forest in this hemisphere, one called dry. In Costa Rica there are efforts underway to replant it. Here in Sonora it persists. Here is the world center of that oddity of everyone's childhood, the Mexican jumping bean. Fierce wild pepper plants grow to the size of small trees. It all seems very strange at first.

When Hernán Cortés hit the beach, more than 550,000 square kilometers of this type of forest, dry tropical, flourished on the Pacific Coast from Panama north to Sonora. Today, less than two percent of it is intact enough to matter and less than about 480 square kilometers has official conservation status. Almost everywhere it is gone and in southern Sonora it is going. But it is still here and it is so very near. Some experts think our best chance of saving any of the dry tropical forests is in this exact place.

The forest is that essential fact that confronts all human beings at the end of the twentieth century, an image of the promise we have betrayed and a chance to redeem ourselves from our folly. It is not an environmental issue, it is not an ecological crisis, but we speak of it by using those terms. It is something deeper, a beating heart that we have not yet stilled and that thunders loudly in the dark hours of the night when we toss and dream about what we have wrought. I think the forest is the world we have left but the world we cannot escape unless we are willing to commit suicide. All over the planet we now face various remnants of the world that created us. And all over the planet we must decide, deliberately or casually, whether to kill the things that formed us and that, I believe, still keep us alive. We are not gods by a long shot, but, by chance, we live at a time when we can make godlike mistakes.

The directions to this forest are as tidy as those on a box of breakfast cereal. To get there is about an eight-hour drive from the border on a four-lane highway (the last thirty miles two-lane). Alamos, a city of six thousand, has the finest examples of colonial architecture in the Mexican north, plus modern hotels (hiding in the disguise of eighteenth-century buildings), restaurants, guides, a state museum devoted to Sonoran culture, and other conveniences. Anyone visiting the forest will most likely make Alamos his or her base.

Everything this book describes is in the sierras and countryside around Alamos, in the vast drainages of the ríos Fuerte and Mayo. After Alamos, the roads are dirt, or sometimes not roads at all but trails for burros and mules. The town has a paved runway for private aircraft. Commercial flights land at Obregon, seventy miles away. The passenger train stops at Navojoa, thirty miles away—usually at some ungodly hour of the night. It is not quite as simple as going down to the corner store. But then, why should it be?

This is the secret forest, one largely unknown to Mexicans in the cities, ignored by governments, lacking cachet for very many scientists, and beneath the notice of American global tourists. It violates too many current articles of faith. It is not distant, so no one suspects it could be tropical. It is not a national park, so few think it is worth a look. It is not a tourist attraction, so it does not attract. The campesinos know the forest root and branch. They go to it for food, for medicine, for building material, for wages, and for comfort. Their trails crisscross all its ground. Here *man and nature* becomes a silly phrase, a distinction without meaning in the forest itself. Here it is people in nature, or better yet, simply nature, a world that consumes all living things and means all living things. There are few guidelines. The venison I am eating under the portal is from a beast taken down because someone with a gun saw it. Seasons mean something for the corn, not for the hunters. The trees get cut without permits. The days go by without clocks. No one seems to have any money. Work can be hard—Ramona's son-in-law walks his cattle twenty-five miles a day in the mountains. He goes on foot because the ground is too hard for a horse. And he dreams of owning a color television. There is very little to do except exist, something that seems increasingly hard to do in the world I hail from.

Today there are so many concerns that we are asked to address—ecological tourism, for example. Is it a violation of the life of local people? Does it distort their world and corrupt them in some sly, Birkenstock way? And then there is conservation. Should not the campesinos be booted off this ground and a refuge be made for the animals and plants? And what about pollution? All that automobile exhaust and mayhem people will create if they come here? And. . . . Well, the list of concerns can become very long.

We are entering a new age, one where we cease to collect sights, one where we finally begin to learn lessons. Tourism, that dismissed and often scorned

notion, will become a kind of survival drill. We will no longer dutifully
check off the art galleries, the cathedrals, the four-star restaurants. Instead,
we will make probes in order to learn how to live. We will visit people who
know how to live in ways we have forgotten or ways we never knew in the
first place. We will talk to trees, listen to rocks, take in lectures from birds,
snails, rats, and spiders. We will do this in order to find the way home, the
way to make a home, keep a home, and cherish a home. When we are
finished, well, then the word tourism will fall dead from our lips and the
consumerism of travel will end. We will have made our pilgrimage, found
that piece of some true cross, planted it in our own gardens, watched it grow,
and, finally, some fine afternoon, we will sit under its fine shade.

I know only a few things for certain. The venison stew with chilis is very
good. Ramona has a smile like a Madonna in an ancient painting. This last
fact intrigues me—when she was a child she saw an uncle beat her twin
brother to death (an uncle who continues to live in her village), and still she
smiles, and still she admires her daughter in her new, black, sexy tube top.
And she might pray for me.

I also know that the forest is being destroyed, devoured by a human wave
that is everywhere on this planet now. And finally I know, and I cannot
prove this point, that the forest will disappear unless something happens for
these people, unless something makes the trees and mountains worth more
alive, than they are worth as lumber, as mineral, as loot. And that the forest
can no more survive without the people than they can without the forest.
They have become one. This has taken more time than anyone can measure,
whether it be the oldest person in the village or the wisest anthropologist on
earth.

❖

The amapa trees burned pink on the hillside but I did not know their
names then. Clouds of butterflies drifted past and I sensed I could never catch
up with them or go the distance they would make. Campesinos suddenly
emerged from the forest with an easy, soft step and the machetes clutched in
their hands seemed a part of their flesh.

The schools have had their paws on me and I could repeat the names of
many things but the words seemed oddly hollow, a foreign language floating
over but not touching a living thing. I carried field identification guides, and
was careful of the water. One night during a summer rain I heard a loud
drumming, an almost thunderous sound, and in the big leaves of a banana
tree found a small green frog signaling its lust. I am the uncommitted. When I
walk in the mountains, every small shrub I pass has bet its life on a few
square meters. I can not duplicate that sensation.

I am a fool here. This fact is not unusual in life but the admission is. One day up on the mountain I ran into a man cutting wood while a couple of curs snarled by his legs. He looked at me with caution—I had come down a slope where there was no trail. We talked and things grew warmer. I repeated what I had been told in the town, that a jaguar had been detected on the mountain. The man looked at me sharply and said, "That is a lie. Nothing happens on this mountain that I do not know about." He did not seem to be speaking from pride but from simple fact. And I quickly retreated to my true station in these woods.

I sensed I had wandered into that house we call ecology, a place that pretends to be carefully mapped but always turns out to be a labyrinth. The structure may have an edge but it seems to have no center. The forest is a question that we will never answer. The birds are screaming along the river, the butterflies pass on unannounced errands, the trees have so many names and shapes, the orchids are hiding up the canyons, safe on cliff walls. The tracks and other marks of the local people are everywhere—the old heap of stones of a trail shrine, the shiny and empty bag of potato chips.

I will tell you of an old man and an old woman I keep revisiting in the forest. They live on a rocky hill in a house without glass windows, the walls a hit-and-miss affair, and in the main their home is open to the land beyond their hearth. They have their problems: Their land is in dispute with a large owner. They have very little money also. But that is not why I go to them. Two military macaws live with the old couple. Not in cages, not chained to perches, but living free. At night they roost in the house and since it is open, they fly in and out at will. During the day, they coast down the river, feeding in the trees and chattering to each other. Sometimes the old woman goes out front with an old tortilla and the macaws storm in, land on a post, and eat from her hand. She has never named them.

Once when I came they were gone and I asked where they were.

She laughed and said, "They are out working."

I keep coming back. I suppose it is something about seeing large birds, free still, tolerating human beings. And then there is the brilliant color of their plumage and the old woman's good temper and a kind of pride she takes in her fellow lodgers. I'm really not sure.

Sometimes people I know will ask me why I go to the forest.

I never answer.

There may be a name for everything.

But there are some things that make words look brittle and small.

Consider the word *forest,* for example. At six letters, the word seems hardly enough. So we try *thorn forest, tropical forest, short-tree forest,* and so forth.

Military macaws

Mexican leaf frog

Opposite: Flowering Echinocereus scheeli *hanging from rock and mountain lichens in the Chalaton drainage.*

A grandmother and grandson rest on a strangler fig
taking over their home near Alamos.

We delight in drawing borders, setting limits, defining cages for the living things that taunt our efforts at comprehension. We have a great need for maps (I certainly do), so that we can hold entire worlds in our frail hands. And we like, sometimes even insist on, clearly marked trails.

After all, we are only human.

❖

The lowlands of the west coast of Mexico are either arid or semiarid almost throughout their entire extent. The very arid region which faces the Gulf of California in northern Sonora merges into an arboreal desert in the vicinity of Guaymas. Near the southern boundary of Sonora this gives way in turn to an arid thorn forest. . . . In the remarkably short distance of 70 miles in southern Sonora may be witnessed the transition from the continental desert, extending 1500 miles to the north, and the coastal thorn forest, extending 1200 miles to the south.

> Forrest Shreve, "Foreword," *Río Mayo Plants: A Study of the Flora and Vegetation of the Río Mayo, Sonora,* Howard Scott Gentry (Washington, D. C.: Carnegie Institution of Washington, 1942).

❖

Morning seeps through the canopy of leaves as the water tumbles down a rock chute. Across the small stream, a painted image of the Virgin watches from the side of a flat rock under the shade of an amapa tree. I have waited months for that tree to bloom and now it is finally in bud. There are no signs marking the way to this shrine and the way through the forest is unclear. Huge figs with drooping, aerial roots dominate the channel. Just past the Virgin a mango tree grows and on the hill above are the stone ruins of an old hut. Someone dreamed of home and hearth and getting up in the morning and picking ripe fruit. Now that dream is over, the people are gone, but the tree clearly does not care. I can hear the tinkling of bells on the necks of goats browsing on the slope overhead. I am thirty miles from the dry collision of barbed trees that Forrest Shreve spoke of as thorn forest but I am in another world, one hardly studied, a carpet of trees flooded with light. The scholarship here is scant and the visitors are few. The life lurking in the sierras and barrancas is known by the campesinos who live here, but barely acknowledged by those of us from the outside. It is a place thronged with trees that for most of the year drop their leaves and look barren. Cold does not trigger this change, but rather the end of the summer rains. Fall does not mean the coming of the snows, but the relentless blaze of the sun.

A thousand feet below lies the small city of Alamos, a failed silver center with as many ghosts as residents. In the facing sierra, perhaps ten miles away, a pine forest intermingles with palms. On those slopes is a cave with human hand prints in the wall left by a bandit named Mano Pinto, a Robin Hood figure to the campesinos—one of many such clouded heroes. He is buried in the woods under a pile of rocks at the place where the *federales* killed him. There are many such places, just as there are many such shrines to the Virgin. A few miles above me on the mountain are cycads, plants that brushed the beginning of time, and in the trees near the top, military macaws flash through the leaves. Just a few hundred yards past the shrine to the Virgin, dozens of orchids grow on the cliffs and there is a side canyon where waterfalls descend into dark grottos of stone. A short way downstream is a shrine to Christ—a barely sketched form on a boulder. And then there is the black outline of a church, its meaning unclear, its location not easily found. I cling to these landmarks, these human details as safe harbors in the endless roll of trees.

Large columnar cacti penetrate the green mat of the forest, a mat with four to five thousand perennials an acre. The numbing complexity of the rain forest and the tropical forest, which begins far to the south, makes its northern stand at this spot. That is one way to look at it. The other is that I am sitting on a rock in the southern end of the Sonoran desert. That vast hot dry sprawl to the north is the tropical forest in disguise, the species from far south cloaked in thorns, hiding as fierce cactus, the dry bony probe of an almost equatorial impulse into harsh and dangerous ground. I feel I am at home, even though this home seems to have no accepted name. This is also the haunt of the jaguar, the lion, the boa, the armadillo, the beaded lizard, the coati, the deer. And the people of the *campo*. There are thousands of square miles of such country where the children of the campo know more about the uses and values of various plants than do trained adults in modern industrial cultures. The forest and people exist as one entity, the various species of flora and fauna have been playing against the hands of *Homo sapiens* here for a very long time. The hills are still dotted with small corn fields, the product of slash and burn agriculture. In a world that worries, justifiably, of the destruction of the great tropical rain forests, here is another rich natural system close by and also little known, and also just as likely to slip away. The concept of an uninhabited park such as practiced in the United States would make little sense here—it would be like putting a guitar in a glass case. The instrument would be preserved for a brief while but the music would die. We tend to call such places the Third World but here they seem more like the first world, the place we all came from and perhaps the place we will all return to after our brief binge of eating, drinking, and looting.

This mass of trees is sometimes called the short-tree or dry tropical forest, which lies on the wet side of thorn forest, a term Howard Scott Gentry, the pioneering botanist of the region, noted "carries a loose rather than a precise meaning, thus often covering a multitude of sins." Whatever the sins lurking in the term *thorn forest,* the same may be said of *dry tropical forest.* But the place is unmistakable, a wonderful collision of desert, and tropics and sierra, a meeting place of biological worlds. Even the untrained eye can sense diverse life forms lapping up against one another. For a biologist, this melding of systems is a fistful of Latin names. For me, it is huge cactus fighting for light against the canopy of the enveloping forest. That is the first image that struck me—giant cactus poking green arms up above the trees.

In the summer the forest is as lush as a jungle. During the dry season, the hills have a barren look with armies of dead sticks standing guard on them. It is, in short, a tropical forest where the force of life sometimes hides and then with the summer rains explodes with exuberance. The June sun blazes against slopes and seems to say that life will never ever return, that death has stolen the land forever. And then with San Juan's Day on June 24 the rains according to legend begin to creep in, the corpse stirs, the hills rustle and turn green, the parrot overhead suddenly seems to make sense, the orchids, well, the orchids belong.

The cycle begins again, the sun forest bewitches all eyes, the boa glides.

Sonoran spiny-tailed iguana.

Chalaton drainage shaded by strangler fig

Opposite: Strangler fig roots encase a boulder

Sierra de Alamos catches the sunrise above the Río Cuchujaqui.

ONE

Some Beginnings

THE PEGS FOR THE HARP'S STRINGS are dark *brasil* wood, the box is *cedro,* the strips anchoring the strings to the box are *guásima,* the bridge is *pino,* the curved back holding the strings is *chino,* and the inlay for decoration is *beraco.* The strings themselves look to be fishing line for the higher end of the scale. The bass notes apparently spring from something that looks a lot like ordinary clothesline. Valente Hurtado Almanea explains this as we sit in the shade of the porch by his workshop. His wife smiles nearby and his young daughter watches with wide eyes and never smiles at all. He lives in a barrio of San Bernardo, a small town that marks the point where the coastal plains and ranges end, and the large bones of the Sierra Madre begin. He is a Warihio, a tribal grouping that was lost to sight for a century or two and then brought back into the light of day—as light is defined by our books and learning—by Howard Scott Gentry when he stumbled upon the culture during his botanical investigations of the Río Mayo area in the 1930s.

"The land of the Warihio," Gentry wrote, "consists of barrancas, arroyos, canyons, steep stony slopes, and cliffs that darken streams or rim the old volcanic mountain tops. It is an enormous succession of diverse terrain shut into a wilderness secrecy, whose every regional door is an arduous 'camino.'"

He found no towns, just hamlets with houses scattered and barely in sight of each other—what is called ranchería culture. At that time, the Warihio families were dotted over about two thousand square miles and numbered perhaps fifteen hundred souls. They were a people who lived geographically, and by their habits, half way between the Tarahumaras mountaineering above them in the pines, and sedentary Mayos below them on the rich river bottoms. Jesuits had found them in the seventeenth century and then, after a short while, they had slipped away.

"Warihios," he continued, "are solitary people, undesirous of even their neighbors's company except in the social vehicle, the *turwuri* rituals. Related families commonly live in the same locality, each with a house from a hundred yards to a league apart . . . . Yet in some cases Warihios have collected together in Mexican towns, as in San Bernardo, where they have been broken to the gregarious Mexican existence . . . ."

As Valente beams and talks, he seems unbroken by the gregarious Mexican existence but this is a matter beyond my judgement since I do not know the world that came before this time. In his workshop, an open Bible lies on a rostrum he built himself, alongside toy trucks he makes for children. In one way, he is an absolute link to the past—after all he is a Warihio, a descendant of the upper Río Mayo's native stock—and in another way he is absolute proof of the changes. He makes harps and violins for the fiestas. These instruments came to his people through the Tarahumara and the Mayos, who in turn got their ideas of the designs from Spaniards and Mexicans. His uncle is a maker of such things and the instruments and the music are central to the Warihio turwuri rituals, a ceremony of both absolution and earthly salvation that in part involves drinking a lot of the native-made alcohol.

But Valente learned his craft, not from his uncle, but at the local government school for Indians. He was taught this skill in a federal effort to bolster native culture. And whereas once a harp, such as the one standing before us, was glued together with the juice of orchids, this one is cemented with store-bought adhesive. Valente knows of the old practices and nods toward the sierra and says, yes such things were once gathered. But he does not. When I ask him to play the harp, he demurs and instead puts on a cassette of Warihio music recorded at a fiesta. We sit there and listen to the beat of the drum, or *tambor,* the singing of the violin, and the dominant chording of the *arpa,* the harp.

The harp itself is the forest singing. Most of its woods come from the local slopes and canyon bottoms. It is not a symbol of man's relationship to nature here. It is the fact—a fact perhaps eroding, but still lingering in the hands and minds and appetites of the local people. Here the forest is still capable of giving all because until quite recently—the last thirty or forty years—the forest was all there was. Even now there is a Warihio village above San Bernardo that is thirteen hours by jeep and then a four-hour walk. In Valente's workshop one of his violins is hanging from a hook, a tree branch with the bark carefully peeled. It descends from the ceiling like a pure white hand with bony fingers. The chairs we sit on he made from guásima wood. And so forth.

We are not speaking here of Eden or some wondrous balance of man and nature that announces the peace of God. The forest, like any place where life exists, is constantly changing and some of these changes have more the look of war than harmony. In the past few years, a new grass, "buffel" *(Pennisetum ciliare)* has been introduced from South Africa and almost overnight whole sections of the forest disappear beneath the blows of the machete and the rich variety of plants is supplanted by this seemingly indestructible grass. All this work so that cattle may flourish and more meat may be produced for those in the cities and the United States. With each swing of a machete now, the harp of the forest grows more still.

But memory and use still walk the land. What Gentry recorded a little over a half century ago can still be seen, is still lived. Here we find people living at the northern limits of the tropical forest in an intimacy with the landscape that is dead even to memory in the United States. The árbol del fuego *(Delonix regia)*, a large tree with flaming red flowers (an introduction to the New World from Madagascar), produces a large pod the Mayos use for rattles. The taavachin *(Caesalpinia pulcherrima)*, a shrub three to nine feet high and a mixture of vermilion and yellow, provides flowers for clouds of butterflies and hummingbirds and the local people make a wash from its roots that they find good for snake and insect bites. Palo dulce *(Eysenhardtia polystachya)* grows nine feet high. The wood is very hard and strong and good for the handles of tools. The cebollín *(Allium scaposum)* is a wild onion with white and purple flowers. People eat the bulbs.

So there is a sense of eternity here, and yet a relentless sense of change and loss. In the thirties Gentry noted this same sensation. He discovered what he thought might be the last of a culture: "the Tepahue of the northern Río Cedros. These last may still be represented by a group of families encountered a few miles south of Tesopaco, who said they were not Mayos or Mexicans proper, that they did not know just who they were, that their progenitors had a spoken tongue of their own, but that not one among them any longer knew any part of it. Puebloans of Tesopaco referred to them as 'coyotes' and treated them rudely generally. They live only a several miles above the settlement of Tepahue."

And of course there is the music, the noise of life itself. A primary instrument is rain. Here rain is a fickle God, just regular enough to instill hope, just erratic enough to feed fear. Time here, and to a large degree life, is based on the rains, as it has always been. "The average yearly rainfall," Gentry noted, "is between 20 and 25 inches . . . . Most of it falls in two seasons; the winter rains, 'las equipatas,' and the summer rains, 'las aguas.' Normally these summer rains start the latter part of June and last into the first part of September. Often rain follows daily rain, each coming at about the same hour in the afternoon. There may be summer dry periods of a week or two duration, when the faces of people will turn earnestly toward the high billowing thunderheads over the sierras, hoping for the cooling rain to come and release the heavy heat growing stronger day by dry day. It is the great growing season of all plants, wild and cultivated, so that all life turns as on a pivot to the thunder of 'las aguas.'"

As Valente and I listen to a tape of Warihio music *las aguas* have ended and we await with more and more anticipation for *las equipatas,* the equal steps that signify the even and less violent rains of winter. The forest is still dropping its leaves to become dead looking until late next June. Not because of cold—the nights in early December still hardly justify a fire—but largely because of moisture, the lack of moisture as the earth dries out. There are blooms on the slopes, the pink amapa and the morning-glory tree, and these episodes of color explode from leafless trees. Every month now will host different species of trees, almost all leafless, as they each in turn are seized with a fury for flowering. The forest never seems without flowers, or butterflies. This is the magic garden lacking both a gardener and the need of a hose.

When you come, you will not see this at first. The forest will begin to crowd the road as you climb from Navojoa on the coastal desert and the trees will look very short and scrubby. The mountains, to be sure, will rise high above and boast columns of stone lancing into the sky but even they will not seem so large and imposing. Likely as not, it will be winter and the leaves will have fallen, presenting the eye with slopes of stripped trees. Eventually, Alamos will come into view, first the tower of the church poking above the hills, then the town itself, the cobbled streets lined with old stucco buildings painted white. Here and there bananas, papayas, and mangos will reach above the garden walls. And it will be very quiet, the ancient narrow streets inhibiting herds of cars. A burro will walk in front of your bumper. The forest itself will envelop the town, its fingers reaching in here and there. It will be a brooding presence that you will at first forget in your excitement to explore the various *calles* (streets) and plazas of the community. And then in time, the forest will come for you. You will see an orchid growing on a tree in someone's *jardín,* and be told it came from the forest. You will sit in a handmade chair, hewn with nothing but a machete, and be told the wood came from the forest. There will be wild peppers, honey, and jellies in the public market, all the fruit of the forest. Eventually, you will go out there and beginning at that moment, life will never again be either so complicated as it was before. Or so simple.

Like the harp made by Valente Hurtado Almanea the forest will at first seem roughly similar to other things, reassuring in a fine and lovely way. The strings will produce a song unlike other songs but not unrelated. The different woods in the instrument will have various new names, but still have a look and feel like other woods from your past. And the people you meet will laugh quite often and smile more than you are most likely used to experiencing. You will discover a kind of mirror in which you can see yourself and recognize yourself and yet you now look somewhat different. This has happened here for a long time—there are centuries of recorded encounters.

The day I picked up the harp from Valente, he and I and some friends went to visit another Warihio who made masks for the *pascola* dancers, a key element in the fiestas. The house was down by an arroyo on the edge of San Bernardo. Roses bloomed in the swept yard and there were citrus trees. The green was vivid and waxy against the dun color of the winter hills. The man sat in back under a tree, carving the masks from wood on a bench. He had a row of six, all staring blankly at the heavens through open eyes, the mouths opened and the teeth bared. A small border of black decoration outlined each face and from the eyebrows and chin, long strands of hair plucked from the tails of cows drooped down. All in all, the masks displayed a visage not of this world yet recognizably rooted in a human origin. I held one to my face and looked out through it. Valente and his friend laughed very hard. And I kept on looking from this new point of view.

❖

There is no way to escape the past, even the obliteration of memory does not help because the dead hands and the ancient deeds ride in our genes and in the cells of the creatures that surround us. Once a Mexican showed me a two-hundred-year-old deed to his rancho. The long document was a series of notations about odd rocks, various streams, and giant trees, all objects used to determine his boundaries. Many of the things cited by the eighteenth-century men who did the survey no longer existed, not even a moldering stump. Should he burn the old document, the marks of earlier people would still be on his ground, and he just would not be aware of what helped form the forest he lives in. That is why anyone who wishes to get a handle on the botany of this place must consider the biography of people who have been bones and dust for centuries, people who never saw this place or knew its name.

People like the Admiral of the Ocean Sea.

We don't really know his exact name, we guess at his nationality, we debate exactly where he sailed, we argue about what he thought he found. In English, we refer to him as Christopher Columbus; in Spanish, as Cristóbal Colón. But we all agree that after centuries of forgotten mariners brushing against these shores, his voyages mark a real beginning for Europeans in this place. On his Fourth Voyage the Admiral was almost deranged. His colony in the Carribean had gone berserk. He had been in jail and in chains. And yet he sensed he had stumbled over a cliff and was falling helplessly into a new book of history. A spirit, an apparition came to him one night in 1502 and spoke words and Columbus wrote them down carefully:

When He saw thee of an age at which He was content, marvelously did He cause thy name to resound throughout the land. The Indies so rich a portion of the world, He gave thee for thine own, and thou hast divided them as it pleased thee, for He gave thee the power to do so. Of those barriers of the Ocean Sea which were closed with such mighty chains, He gave thee the keys, and thou wast obeyed through many lands, and thou hast gained an honorable fame throughout Christendom.

Kirkpatrick Sale, <i>The Conquest of Paradise: Christopher Columbus and the Columbian Legacy</i> (Alfred A. Knopf, New York, 1990), 6.

The Europeans who came to this new ground were not the only ones bestirred by visions. In the beginning, we are of two minds. Those who have lived here for a very long time have thoughts about the ground, the trees, the flowers. They write them down as poems, sing them as songs, carve them as images in stone. The other way of seeing this place comes from Europe on ships, is firm in its beliefs and whatever its deep wells of compassion, cannot accept the ideas of the people found here. This other mind burns records, overturns temples, and sees the forest as the realm of darkness, the house of devils. We have never resolved these two minds and when we move about they travel with us as quarrelsome guests in our heads. We have tried every possible way to avoid facing this conflict: conservation, national parks, zoos, reserves for native people, films, paintings, books. Our modern fascination with nature is a way to avoid this brutal past. We think that if we make a place for nature our acts will be forgiven and our appetites permitted. So nature is sequestered on the coffee table, safe from the roar of our city streets.

> I? Who am I?
> I live as a fugitive, singer of flowers.
> Songs I make,
> and butterflies of song.
> They bloom in my soul
> so that my heart may savor them.

An Indian poem written before the conquest, in Irene Nicholson, <i>A Guide to Mexican Poetry,</i> Minutiae Mexicana Series (1968; reprinted, Mexico, D.F.: Editorial Minutiae, 1988), 7.

The devil has provided himself here on earth with a thick wood full of pitfalls, there to hide and prepare his plans in secret as do wild beasts and poisonous snakes. This wood and these pitfalls are the songs he has inspired for his service . . . .

Fray Bernardino de Sahagún, Florentine Codex,
commenting on Indian poetry before the preconquest, ibid, 13–14.

Of course, the past is not all poems and visions. Surprisingly, a good deal of it turns on the location of a few precious metals of slight utility. We seldom question this fact because we still clank along wearing the chains of this past. Hernán Cortés was the great Captain; Hernán Cortés was the great monster. Hernán Cortés was and is a part of us, an element in our being that keeps us pushing always over the next hill, looking for that heart of gold. After sacking Mexico, he is still hungry. And so he sits in his palace and writes the Spanish king of rumors he has heard of the north, of the blank on his map where Alamos will ultimately be founded:

> Between the north coast and the province of Mychuacan there is a certain tribe called the Chichimeca. They are a very barbarous people and not so intelligent as those of the other provinces. I am likewise now sending sixty horsemen and two hundred foot soldiers together with many of our native allies to investigate that province and its inhabitants. I have given my men instructions that if they discover in these people some aptitude or ability to live as others do and to be instructed in the knowledge of Our Holy Faith and to recognize the service which they owe to Your Majesty, they are to make every effort to pacify them and bring them under Your Majesty's Yoke; they are also to settle among them in whichever place seems most convenient. If, however, they find that they are not as I have said above and refuse to be obedient, the Spaniards are to make war on them and reduce them to slavery; so that there may be no part remaining of all this land which does not serve and obey Your Majesty. By making slaves of this barbarous people, who are almost savages, Your Majesty will be served and the Spaniards will benefit greatly, as they will work in the gold mines and perhaps by living among us some of them may even be saved. . . . And I am certain that land will soon be settled for we have heard that it is very rich in silver.

Hernán Cortés, Fifth Letter, *Letters From Mexico*, trans. and ed. Anthony Pagden
(New Haven: Yale University Press, 1986), 446.

❖

After the men of the sword came the men of God such as Father Eusebio Francisco Kino. Rich mines have been found at Alamos and the priest sees opportunities for spreading the faith, and yet is sick at heart at the corruption of riches we all so easily succumb to. This treasure will fuel a Spanish thrust to the north that had largely stalled on the West Coast since about 1540 when Coronado, dreaming of seven cities of gold, had marched as far as

Kansas. Kino was a man with imagination. He once proposed pushing into what is now Arizona as mere prelude to his ultimate ambition, Japan. It is February 15, 1687 and Kino writes in a fury:

> . . . Some whom I have met have related prodigies of their plentiful and rich metals . . . .Yesterday and the day before yesterday, in order to reach the holy mission of Conicari, I passed through the mines of Los Frayles themselves . . . and I have just seen and recognized most palpably how very clearly and certainly are verified the words of the new and very Catholic royal cédula of his Majesty, God spare him . . . . And it cannot have happened without particular disposition of the sovereign Lord that, at the same time that with Catholic funds, his Majesty during these four or five years has sent us to the conquest and conversion of the Californias, here in the very sight of the same Californias, there should be discovered such wealth that many prudent men unanimously acknowledge and confess that they have not seen such treasure anywhere in the country thus far discovered . . . . Many more mines can be opened . . . .

Father Eusebio Francisco Kino, February 15, 1687, in Herbert E. Bolton,
Rim of Christendom: A Biography of Eusebio Francisco Kino, Pacific Coast Pioneer
(New York: The Macmillan Company, 1936), 239–40.

A century later, Fray Antonio Reyes comes over from Spain with his two nephews and makes Alamos the seat of his bishopric. The boys settle in and become the leading symbol of the silver wealth and bear the name Alemada. But Fray Reyes, while he enjoys his palace off the Plaza de las Armas, realizes that there will be a price for this drive toward wealth. Years earlier he wrote about the disease that possesses men in this New World:

> They establish mining camps and villages with flimsy houses and cheap furniture, which are abandoned without difficulty or loss whenever the occasion arises. That is why in the province of Sonora there is not a single decent, permanent Spanish settlement, and it is distressing to see the multitude of deserted villages and ruined mining camps, not because they are lacking in rich minerals, but due to the ambition and greed of the settlers who hope to obtain greater profit in the new discoveries.

Fray Antonio Reyes, O. F. M., Sonora Manifesto, April 20, 1772,
The First Bishop of Sonora, ed. Albert Stagg
(Tucson: University of Arizona Press, 1976), 38.

Note how the forest is barely mentioned in the early documents. Nature is not yet a subject that interests many of us. When at odd moments the rich tangle of trees and the people who live in them with ease finally come to our notice, this sudden awareness causes alarm. Father Ignez Pfefferkorn, a Jesuit, toils bravely for years, bringing Christ to the residents. And this is what he notices about the biological riches that surround him:

> It is not difficult for a Sonoran to prolong a war or to perpetuate it indefinitely. They are amply supplied with food as well as with war equipment from their storehouse, the forest. There they find animals, wild fruits, and roots for their sustenance, as well as all the materials for making new weapons. Beds are at all times ready for them, for they require only a place on the bare earth for the night's rest. If they are driven out of a district, they immediately occupy another, and there again they find all necessities.

Observation on Sonora (1794–1795) by Father Ignaz Pfefferkorn,
Sonora: A Description of the Province, trans. and annotated Theodore E. Treutlein
(Albuquerque: University of New Mexico Press, 1949), 209.

It is not right for us to scorn this past since we are still in the very earliest phase of a recovery from it. We sit on a hillside and cannot name the trees, there are simply too many. We look up and cannot name the butterflies, they are too colorful. We walk through the forest and forget the need for names as the flowers hang over our heads. We are on the edge of finding a place. We begin to notice.

> Here one finds a variety of the most important or typical trees of the dry tropical habitats in the New World, trees and habitats unknown north of the border ("la linea"). The rich mixture of trees fifteen to borty feet tall includes the following species at or near their northern limit: "pochote" or kapok of the genus *Ceiba;* "guajilote" *(Bombax);* "Brasil" *(Haematoxylon);* "amapa" *(Tabebuia);* "palo barril" *(Cochlospermum);* "mauuto" *(Lysiloma);* "tescalama" and other fig trees including strangler figs *(Ficus);* "hecho" and other columnar cacti *(Pachycereus, Stenocereus);* eight species of "torote" including gumbo limbo *(Bursera);* the famous Mexican jumping bean or "brincador" *(Sebastiana)* and over one hundred other trees, shrubs and vines of the New World tropics . . . .
>
> Wild figs especially attract many species of parrots and a variety of fruit-eating bats. Other tropical wildlife includes mot-mots, trogons, magpie jays, military macaws, casque headed frogs, boa constrictors, indigo snakes, vampire bats, murine opossums and in the wildest barrancas, the jaguar ("El Tigre").

Paul S. Martin, naturalist of the Río Mayo

❖

The treasure is real, the loot is enormous, the riches possess and almost break our backs. And we can never quite let go of the stories, or cease marveling at the way our heart quickens when faced with cold, precious metal. "The vein is at least thirty feet wide, one half of which is worked, and sixty thousand dollars are said to be taken from it monthly!" wrote Lieutenant R. W. H. Hardy in the 1820s.

The silver bars were brought from the mines on the backs of mules and stored in a large room in the big house. They were piled rows upon rows there . . . . At meals the whole family sat at a long, long table and the whole dinner set was silver, even the cups and saucers and tumblers. As the years passed, with wear and tear the silver dishes were all dented, and my grandmother and her younger sister hated them. They longed to have some china dishes or at least drinking glasses like other families had, but their father would not hear of it. Whenever a servant dropped a dish, he would exclaim, "Dos reales a la bolsa," which meant two bits in his purse. For if it had been china, it would have broken. One day my grandmother somehow got hold of a small glass and kept it hidden in her bedroom like something precious . . . . At one time her father wanted to put silver bars in the windows instead of iron ones, but the authorities stopped him because robbers might make off with them.

> Memory of Mrs. Carmen Karam, 1948, of how her grandmother,
> daughter of silver baron José Maria Alamada,
> lived in Alamos in the nineteenth century.

Everything changes, yet nothing changes. Tribes disappear, wars come and go, new rules are laid down, various notions of progress, of conversion are pushed. And yet a bedrock always remains, one that bedevils many who come here to make things change.

The *toma ani* (money world) also provides a focus for Mayo gossip. Concealed near the ocean in the sand hills not far from Banari, a place of buried treasure glows at night. If one digs up this treasure without the proper ceremonial precautions, a swarm of *cicialim*, terrible black batlike creatures causing sickness, is released. The cicialim will follow each piece of money wherever it goes, from person to person even to the innocents, the little children. A person may safely take the money from the toma ani only if he first has a dream wherein the soul of the person who buried the money appears. The deceased must ask him to dig up the treasure, telling him where and how to get it. If one uses it to give a pasko, in fulfillment of a manda made by the deceased, the danger is lessened. But it is always a dangerous business, and generally only those with evil motives are said to attempt it . . . .

> N. Ross Crumine, *The Mayo Indians of Sonora: a people who refuse to die*
> (1977; reprinted Prospect Heights, Illinois: Waveland Press, Inc., 1988), 60.

Now we are here and we begin to look around. We have centuries behind us. We are catalogues of mistakes and insights. The forest presses in and we begin to notice it. The mines have gone dead for a spell and the excited talk of gold and silver has died down. Flowers bloom. The treasure of the Sierra Madre is not so simple as it once was.

❖

This happened years ago, before I came to the forest. In those days I knew this man who seldom spoke and when he did speak, it was often sharply. He worked for years in a small room with no windows and translated documents written by men long dead. His speech was careful, the words almost etched into the air, and his manner displayed a certain weariness with something he could not name. He was no longer a priest but for years he had lived the faith.

He would suddenly erupt with words and say things, well, things like the following: "I took these two Papago boys up to northern Arizona, they'd never been anywhere really, and we went to Navajo Monument, you know, Betatakin and Keet Seel, and we saw everything. They took it all in. I remember at Betatakin one of them said, 'It is a dream.' Anyway, we were driving back and when we were around Casa Grande I heard one of the Papagos say to the other in Papago, 'This is my land.'

"That's the way I feel. This is my land. When I come back, say from the Midwest, and if I'm there more than a week or two I get sick because I can't see the mountains, when I come back—and I know you've read about this in bad novels but I really feel—I want to stop the car and kiss the earth.

"I belong here.

"Let me tell you something. I once was the kind of person who had to read the morning newspaper every day before breakfast. I would go out in the yard and pick it up. If it wasn't there, it upset me. And I would get magazines—*Newsweek, Time,* journals—and I read them and I had to have them. I could not imagine life without them.

"Then I went off and lived with the Indians. It's not like it is now. I lived in little villages, and later in Mexico with Mexicans in little villages. There was no electric light, there wasn't even kerosene. I used candles, sputtering candles.

"Something happened. I don't know how, it wasn't something that came in a regular process, in steps. Look, one morning I was sitting on the ground in front of a wattle and daub hut. My back leaned against it and I could feel every particle of mud and the sticks on my skin and I would move my back and just feel it. It was that part of the morning when the coolness is giving way to heat and stillness. The leaves were just hanging there with a coat of dust, silvery. The yard in front of me was dirt and I could watch lizards scurry across the dust. I just sat there. Every particle of mud and sticks, I could feel them against my skin.

"And it was enough. I didn't need tomorrow or yesterday. I wasn't bored. That's when I knew it had happened. The yard, the hut, the lizards, the light, the air, the dust, the morning—it all had a fullness.

"When I finally had to leave, I felt like an alien.

"I don't know if you can understand this."

Stands of Organ-pipe cacti against a blazing sunset near Alamos, Sonora.

Desert tortoise

A woman in the campo village of Aguas Calientes
washing clothes in the stream.

Opposite: Smooth white granite walls of the Río
Cuchujaqui shine in morning light.

A family in La Higuera with their baby

Opposite: Sunrise filters through hecho cactus to flowering nightshade.

*Pink flowering amapa prieta and white palo blanco
with hecho cactus in the tropical deciduous forest.*

The doorway in Alamos
frames a woman holding
bougainvillea flowers.

Sunrise lights the Church of the Purisma Concepción, seen through the portales of the palacio lining the plaza at Alamos.

Below: Courtyard of hotel Casa de los Tesoros, Sonora.

TWO

The World They Found, Loved, Made

FIRST, THE VOICES, LOUD HAPPY VOICES bouncing off the cobblestones and the old plastered walls of the casas as the procession walks down the narrow lane from the plaza to the campo. Then comes the Virgin riding on a pallet of red and borne on the shoulders of two stalwarts of the faith, the priest trailing in his white robes. Finally, the throng, five or six hundred people on the march at 4 A.M. on a cool November morning. Firecrackers explode, rockets burst overhead and between hymns there is a soft murmuring of voices, of parents and children, old women and men, adolescent couples doing courtship under the mask of devotion. At the head of the procession is a police car, the red light circling on its roof and casting a glow on the serpent of people trailing behind.

The procession is about fifteen-years-old but seems as old as time. I know one of the men who started it. It began with a half dozen couples meeting in the front of the church on the plaza and each year grows larger. The Virgin, a Barbie-doll-sized figure in a glass case, first appeared in this area in 1683. She was sitting on a tall cactus when she was sighted by a group of Indians. When they piled up stones so she could dismount from her thorny tower she flew away. About that time a massive silver strike was made, one that spewed forth wealth for over two centuries. And the adoration began.

The procession seems not very organized. Last night on the plaza, I tried to discover when it would begin and was told 3 A.M., 4 A.M., 5 A.M., 6 A.M. and, when I asked the town cop, was given a shrug that said, "Who knows?" As we walk through the town, it is still asleep and silent, even though ten percent of the population has turned out for the six-mile trek into the forest. Even the dogs are stilled by the unexpected numbers. As we pass the hospital, I can see vaqueros asleep on the floor of the darkened lobby where they bunk to be near their ailing people.

Scattered through the crowd are women carrying children in their arms. Some of the sleeping kids are three- or four-years-old. When they were babies and sick, these women prayed for their lives and vowed if their infants lived they would carry them in the procession for four years. Now they are fine and grown fat and large and the women stagger on under their loads. Here and there are short, dark Indian women clutching bouquets of paper flowers

87

they have made. And there are some old men, bent over with years, yet still capable of marching.

Every once in a while, the whole group stops, two helpers of the priest mount small loudspeakers on the top of their heads and the father's voice booms off over the crowd and explains the hard but good way of Christ. I can almost see the skulls of his helpers resonant like skins on a drum as they clutch the loudspeakers with their hands and hold them firmly on the top of their heads. While the priest speaks, the firecrackers and rockets never stop exploding and no one seems to find this amiss. An old man walking beside me breaks out a half pint of mezcal and takes a warming swig. In the sky above Orion hunts.

After about two miles on the paved highway, we hit the arroyo and turn into the forest. Gray light is just beginning to seep from the east and a dirt track is visible under the arching trees. The birds are yet silent, the trogons hidden in the upper branches. The voices in the crowd still murmur rather than speak but there is an air of gaiety. Soon the stream comes up from the sands and people must scamper back and forth across the waters. The old women are the most agile in their long dark dresses and widow faces. They leap like cats. There are repeated stops for saying the rosary, for speeches, for song. The whole six-mile walk swallows three hours of night and no one hurries or struggles or grows impatient. The Virgin is very kind and she will heal the sick, mend the broken limb, straighten out the pain in one's life. I remember a lunch with one of the original founders of the procession. An American friend of mine asked how anyone could place faith in a virgin, a woman who lacked experience in life, who did not know the ways of the flesh. The man looked with puzzlement at my American friend, and said with a smile, "Well, yes. Because she is a virgin."

About a half mile from the village and its small church, a mariachi band meets the procession at the point where the track leaves the arroyo and enters a lane locked between stone walls. A little further on where the cobblestones lead up to the small hamlet's plaza Mayo dancers and players join the front. The Mayos have been waiting all night, dancing before tiny fires in front of the church and fortifying themselves with tequila. The drummer and flute player has to be revived with a good hit of liquor, and is instantly awake and making music. Around their legs the dancers wear rattles made from the cocoons of the forest's moths. On their face are masks carved from the wood of the forests trees and in their hair, red paper flowers. They are dressed in white long underwear.

The Virgin on her red pallet floats across the plaza, past the stands of food vendors who are ready for the fiesta. She is installed in the church where she will rule for nine days and nights. Men and women and children touch her glass case and cross themselves. Outside, eight feet up on the stone wall of the small iglesia, grows an organ-pipe cactus. It is never watered and it never dies and that is a miracle. Candles burn beneath it.

Now the crowd rests before the big wooden doors of the church, eats food, drinks coffee, and talks. The Mayos revive and music flows from the drum, flute, a violin, and a harp. The violinist is very old and keeps an empty coffee jar full of tequila by his side. When his wife comes over and picks it up, apparently thinking it water, he snatches it back without losing his place in the song. As the Indians take turns dancing a soft but complicated step, people gather round. One spectator is quite drunk and smoking a cigarette, and pushes his way into the circle. He perfectly mimics the steps of the dancer, his head tilted down, his lit cigarette still held in his hand. He becomes a shadow performing perhaps six inches from the costumed dancer. The major domo of the group, an ancient man, very thin and with a dark, lined face, remains expressionless for several moments, then steps forward, taps the volunteer dancer on his shoulder, and makes him move off another six inches. There are rules but they do not seem onerous. One of the Mayo dancers, hidden by his costume and his mask, wears a thick wristwatch and on his chest a T-shirt advertising Vaurnet sunglasses. The man who helped start the procession fifteen years ago jabs my side, and says with delight, "Look at that, look at that."

There is no sign on the highway to this village. There is no announcement posted in the town giving a date and time for the procession to this isolated church. The fiesta is not listed in anyone's calendar of events. In a week, as the fiesta reaches its climax, ten or twenty thousand people will gather here, some having walked thirty or forty miles to fulfill vows. There will be Gypsies showing movies, a freak show, barkers selling blankets, beer stalls, vendors with images of the Virgin, and many dances. Then it will all vanish. Strangers driving by will look at the green, impenetrable mass of trees and vines and silence, and wonder who could live in there and what could ever happen in such a place.

❖

There are memories of things we have never known, experiences that dominate us yet never happened. Places we have never been before, places whose smell and look and feel hurl us back into the dim beginnings. We are very weak at endings, we dread endings, but we are infinitely creative at these beginnings. It is in our blood. We must have these ceaseless beginnings. Or we are finished.

The first time I rode into the sleeping town Alamos, late at night, and looked at the plaza palms and the cathedral in the moonlight, I had a strange sense of having come home. There is a certain vague feeling of familiarity about the spot that has alternately troubled and comforted me. I do not presume to offer any explanations, but that has always been the way I felt about Alamos, and I suppose it shall be, to the end.

John W. Hilton, *Sonora Sketch Book*
(New York: The Macmillan Company, 1947), 69.

What we feel, in part, depends on the time of year. Come May or June and there is an anxiety in the air. The rains, no one believes in the rains any longer. There is dust, heat, glare, and painful dryness. Every face registers these facts and each morning and afternoon eyes scan the sky looking for a puff of cloud. The joints in the chairs come loose, the wood is almost on fire to the touch. We are not alone in this yearning for rain as the days slide toward the beginning of summer. Sometime around San Juan's Day on June 24 the showers begin. The mochomos, the leaf cutter ants *(Atta mexicana)*, have watched also. Normally they build large caverns underground, grow fungus on the leaves their endless columns of workers strip from the forest's trees, and by this act become a primary engine for putting nitrogen into the soil, for recycling the forest so that it may continue. But when the first good rain comes the colonies of mochomos begin to surge into a new level of life. About an hour before dawn they take off, the air is thick with the nuptial flight of ants, and under the lights about town the exhausted lovers will pile up in heaps six inches deep. And then with the sunrise the frenzy ends for another year. New colonies are founded, the blood is increased, the numbers burgeon, and the world of the leaf cutter ant is propelled to a new level for a new season.

For man or beast, for tree or ant, the rains mean so much. The drops fall not on the earth but on a carpet of DNA that has known and remembered rains without number and deep in these codes of double helix there is no hesitation, no wondering about what must be done.

I never remember time by years, only by the rains.

Don Raymundo Robles of Alamos, b. 1904.

The dry seasons are two: that of the spring—March, April, May, and June, and that of the fall—October, November, and possibly half of December. The spring drought is more severe and as it advances the sun grows week by week in intensity; the soil shrinks, cracks, and dust puffs up under foot. Leaves

wither and fall until many plants stand like naked supplicators with mute
uplifted arms. Nearly all life is at this time half hidden under protective masks
against the drought.

Howard S. Gentry, *The Warihio Indians of Sonora-Chihuahua:
An Ethnographic Survey* (Washington, D. C.: Government Printing Office), 82.

Fear is a basic part of any place and the task in any place is to replace this
feeling of fear with one of home. We have so many maps we have almost
forgotten the mystery of the earth. But it is still there, just as it has always
been. During the revolution Martín Luis Guzmán rode the train through
Navojoa and looked over at the sierra and felt what we all do when we see its
green folds rising up off the desert. We all wonder what is up there and in
some part of us, that rich part where our mind plays beyond our commands,
we all dread and lust for what is up there.

. . . The train began its long interminable trip in sight of the awesome blue
sierra between whose crevices ran the white lines of brooks and mysterious
pathways.

"Down there," said those familiar with the terrain, pointing to the whitish
cracks, "the wild Indians descend."

And the rough, the immense sierra, whose greatest beauty lay in the inter-
play of the light with the sharp jags of surface and line, was the subject of
many comments on the contrast between the beauty of its brightness and the
black legend of its barbarous excursions . . . .

The stops were in desolate towns sunk—even the more important, like
Navojoa—in a dense atmosphere of barbarism, incivility, of satisfaction
with the crude, the formless, the primitive and ugly, which made the spirit
shrink . . . . It was the Mexican Far West, newer than that of the United States
and with less promise of industry, less machinery, less energy; with a greater
aboriginal influence, which was revealed in the use of mud as building material, but as barbarous as the other, more so perhaps, its brutality
unrestrained by a tradition of civilization, and ignorant of all the amenities
invented by human culture. The civilizing influence of the Jesuit fathers had not
time to flourish in these regions; currents of authentic savage life still floated in
the tragic, miserable atmosphere, in which every feeble better impulse was
crushed out by the uncontrolled passions of men who responded to nothing
but the zoological stimuli. I felt no surcease of this depressing atmosphere until
the train entered the gentle regions of Sinaloa. Compared with southern
Sonora, even the poorest farms of Sinaloa are outposts of civilization.

Martín Luis Guzmán, *El Aguila y la serpiente,*
[The Eagle and the Serpent], ed. Harriet de Onis
(Garden City, New York: Doubleday & Company, 1965 [1928]), 79–80.

Everything was supposed to end: The forest was to be tamed; the Indians were to be dissolved into some kind of paste and recast as Europeans; the wars were to cleanse the land with fire. It does not always work out according to plan. And no one can see the forest or the trees without reckoning with the people who make the forest flesh.

I was a federal in Colima. We fought a battle there. Men were shot to pieces all over the place. All you could hear was their moans of pain, like one voice. It was terrible. Terrible! There was a man beside me who was dead but had not been buried. Men were just left for the coyotes to eat. My leg was badly wounded and I couldn't move.

I made a manda (religious promise) that if I lived and could return to my home I would pay my promise in the *Hurasim* (men's masked Lenten ceremonial society).

Then when I got here I had to pay my manda. I went to my old grandmother, who was the only relative I had left. I told her I had this promise. She didn't say anything. She just took me to the church. There were only a few charred pieces of cane and one cross standing. I just stood there and looked at it. "What will I do?" I asked. "I must keep my promise." I talked to the old people and they told me what had happened. "The government isn't mad at us," I told them. "It's the priests who have sent all the money to Rome who are mad at us." So they took up a collection to start building a church.

We didn't have bells then. When the church was burned some schoolteachers had taken the bells. . . . A young virgin girl from Huatabampo went to the governor and got a paper that said [we] could have the bells back. She is now called a saint . . . .

Juan recalling the Mexican Revolution in N. Ross Crumine,
The Mayo Indians of Sonora: a people who refuse to die
(Prospect Heights, Illinois: Waveland Press, Inc., 1988 [1977]), 24–25.

Everything was supposed to end . . . .

❖

When I come upon them, he and his wife are walking along the road through the forest in the September sun. The road is fine yellow dust and then at places very hard where it cuts through belts of contera stone. The forest presses against it, dense and green as the rains have just ended. It is seven miles to the river from town but they make this trek once or twice a week without complaint. The man carries a face mask, a jerry-rigged harpoon, and a bolsa. He has small eyes almost buried by his skin, and is called Chino. She has a scarf around her head to protect her skin from the darkening power of the sun's rays. They look to be in their twenties and they pile into the back of the pickup. He is a plasterer but there is no work now, and may not be work for quite a while. It can be like that. They live in a small *jacal* against the mountain with their four children. The kitchen is outside under a ramada, several fruit trees grow here and there, and the whole lot may be fifteen hundred square feet. Water is carried in buckets, light comes from an oil lamp.

When we get to the river, they climb out and he goes to work. He strips to his Levi cut-offs, puts on the mask, and wades into the water. He swims past the cypress clawing the banks with huge roots and soon he is working upstream under the cliffs. Trogons call from the trees. She sits under a blooming red bird of paradise, her face serene with pride. The man works for hours diving in the deep holes again and again. Sometimes he comes over to show her a particular catch and she beams at those moments. By the end of the day, he has speared fifteen or twenty pounds of bass and catfish. He will sell them in his barrio to other *pobres*. All the while he works, his wife never stops watching with that soft smile.

That night we eat fish soup out in his yard under the trees. I come with a friend and we bring cookies and pop for the children. I do not really know how they survive. But once I was walking with him and his small son through the forest and we had to cross a stream. His son had on new tennis shoes, the father wore *huaraches,* sandals. The small boy balked at the stream, hesitant to get his precious new shoes wet. His father jumped the thin strand of water, looked back at the boy with a blank face and said nothing. Then he walked over to a cliff, got a large rock, returned, and pitched it mid-way in the shallow stream. The boy skipped across without a word. When we reached the main river a few hundred yards downstream, a great blue heron lifted off the water and slowly flapped around the bend.

Still, though the forest has born footsteps for thousands of years, we persist in dreaming of the place where no one else has ever been. We will drop into it, plant the first footprint, gaze at innocence, be like lords. There is no such place. In the United States, we can pretend that we can indulge in such fantasies. We now have a nation where few leave the sidewalk and the roadway and when we go off, we can get past trails and signs of our kind at times. But we are never the first to be anywhere, we merely have buried the evidence of those who came before us. In Mexico, the evidence is near at hand. Climb any hill and a trail will suddenly come into view. There will be no signs. It will have no clear purpose at first. But it is impossible not to follow it. Pick any hill.

The caminos of Mexico have no beginning and are without end. For having set out upon a road, one can take up a foot-trail common to pack beasts and men; from this one can branch out upon a side trail connecting dimly to another side trail by deer or cattle path which leads one back by a circuitous route to a main trail. Thus the land is covered with a maze of trails, over plains and valleys, through mountains, deserts and canyons, from seashore to seashore; a young man could grow a grey beard following them and in the end reach only his own grave. Graves, as a word in passing and not as evidence for the above statement, can often be seen along the trails of Mexico; the mounds of stones are like periods to sentences and their little wooden crosses like asterisks suggesting footnotes to lives never written. By the trails also are other mounds of stones bearing crosses at the apex, which in the sentence of life may be likened to commas. In passing these the pious journeyman lifts his hat and tosses on another stone. These heaps of stones, though topped with Catholic cross, preserve nevertheless an old Indian custom.

Howard Scott Gentry, "Caminos of San Bernardo,"
The Michigan Alumnus Quarterly Review (Winter 1942).

We seem to believe that the only place safe from us is the place that lacks any sign of our kind. From this belief comes part of our demand for wilderness. The forest is not such a place. Every time I go into it I am reminded of this simple fact. We have been riding down the back roads half the day looking for plants we do not know and faces we have not yet met. Finally, at noon we stop by a shallow stream, the bank lined with sabinos, or bald cypresses. A local man is with us who lives in El Cajón, a small village where John W. Hilton spent a good deal of time in the 1940s. It is always good to have a local man in the intricacies of the forest. We lunch on cheese, canned meat, tortilla chips, pop, and beer. A few moments before, two deer had floated past our eyes and into the forest. The villages we have visited this day have been very poor and very clean, the small houses whitewashed, the *portales* decked out with plants, the women busy pounding clothes clean on the rocks. The local man feels expansive, what with the food and the beer and the good shade of the trees.

He says, "We do not have much money around here. But we have food and beer." And then he laughs.

Of course, there are other forms of life to consider besides the villagers. No scientist has yet detected these creatures but the people here know of them and swear that they exist. It is night and I sit with a friend and ask him about one such beast. Orchids cling to a chicken-wire screen and the gray-green flower stalks with delicate yellow flowers seem like tongues stroking the black air. Saul will be the watchman at the palacio this night, and he shows off his gun for a moment, then jams the clip back in, and stuffs it back in his pants. He is the hunter, the man of this pueblo who combs the sierra seeking game. He is the man who knows the animals. So I ask him about the *onza,* the lion of the sierra that is not quite a lion. The snout is said to be more like a dog's, the color different, the pad of the feet on the forest floor more mysterious. For decades, Americans have sought the skin of an onza, the skull of an onza, the teeth of an onza. None ever turns up. This troubles no one in the sierra, since every campesino knows that onzas exist. Saul as a matter of fact has killed one. But alas, at the time, he explains, he did not know anyone in the world cared about possessing the remains, so he left the beast to rot in the forest. He says this matter-of-factly, as if the loss were a small detail in a busy life.

I sip my drink, I watch the bats storm the flowers of agaves, and I dream of onzas. The American chunk of the desert has been almost stripped of mystery. It is all maps, rezonings, exact species counts, brokered accounts, blood samples. Computers call up plants and animals, and spatter them in configurations across screens, a ream of metric units spewing from the printer. But south of the line, the desert is by our standards still unknown because most of the knowers are brown. They barely read or write, and wear their knowledge gracefully, something not heavy or ponderous but natural, a wild growth emanating from their heads and twisting with green force much as leaves and tendrils twine out from a hard, rough barked trunk. They do not exist as a source of knowledge because they are seldom quoted in the books and journal articles cranked out by diligent scientists. Of course, on this onza matter they are beneath contempt in the eyes of science. No one believes in onzas except the people of the sierra and the forest. I do not believe in the existence of onzas.

But I do not doubt them either. I can dream about them. The shoulders ripple with muscle yet the cat still moves with simple grace, the big feet making not a sound as it courses through the shadows. The breath is sweet, the mouth warm and cleansed from a drink that very morning in a shady mountain pool. The eyes never rest, the ears swallow whole the noise of the forest, and the cat never skips a beat when a flock of screaming parrots storms past overhead. The doglike snout drinks deeply of the warm air and the teeth gleam and wait, hungry for the warm gush of blood streaming out of a severed neck. In my dreams, the onza never makes a sound, not even a faint purring and I can always feel the hot breath flowing from that mouth, a warm wave lapping against the tendons at the back of my neck.

There is in the woods of Sonora a wild animal about which Spanish opinion there is divided. By some it is called lion, by others, leopard. In my opinion it is neither . . . . The animal is as large as a big dog or wolf and resembles a wildcat or tiger in the shape of its head as well as in the shape of its body. Its paws, likewise, are shaped like the paws of a tiger and are armed with fearful claws. It has short ears but a long, thick tail. The hair which covers its upper body from head to the tip of its tail is reddish grey in color. The entire belly is white, and there is not a single spot anywhere on the animal. Of all beasts of prey there is none which does greater harm to stock raising because it feeds on the slaughtered animal only so long as its real hunger lasts, and when it becomes hungry again it always seeks new prey. In spite of this, it is by nature very timid and flees as soon as it catches sight of a person . . . .

The animal which the Spaniards call *onza* is in shape almost like the animal just described. However, it has a longer body, which is also noticeably thinner and narrower, especially toward the rump. Its feet are shorter, its chest, however, much broader, and I found no difference in color, except that the onza is lighter and somewhat more reddish. It is not as timid as the foregoing animal, and he who ventures to attack it must be well on his guard, because its ability is incomparable. It deals as unmercifully with cattle, horses, and mules as do other beasts of prey and is even more voracious.

Father Ignaz Pfefferkorn, *Sonora,* 1794–1795, p. 109.

Fauna—La fauna de Sonora es rica y veriado . . . . Mamiferos: ordilla, borrego salvaje, berrende, cabra montés, cacomixtle, conejo, coyote, cuyo, gatos montés, jabali, leopardo, leibre, lobo, onza . . . .

Enciclopedia Regional Ilustrada Sonora, Fernández Editores, Mexico, D.F., 1989.

We must not go too far in our learning, although there is probably no way to stop. We are what we are. But even if we must keep on discovering things, measuring things, wondering at things, we must be careful not to throw things away. There are creatures in the forest we can never find, never skin out, never key with our taxonomic tables, and label properly. If we are to preserve a vital, living system, a true world with all its diversity, they also must be saved. Perhaps, the most endangered species are the ones we will never lay eyes on. And we must be very careful to protect them from our books and scorn.

The Carbunco is a small, haired animal, slightly smaller than a house cat, which carries a light in its forehead. There are very few and they come forth from their ground lairs only at night. The light they carry is presumably to enable them to see their prey. It is like a blue stone and emits a bright white light. They are very wild and will run if one approaches, and they will immediately extinguish the light which betrays them and one is unable to follow them. They live in the rocks and just beyond Chorijoa a few have been known to come forth in "las aguas."

Gentry, *Warihio,* 136.

❖

Years ago I ran a magazine and a man came in with a short story and I printed it. The man had lived in Mexico for twenty years, in this exact forest. I had never been to this part of Sonora then and perhaps the story was one of the things that brought me here. The story since then has had a curious history. People who have wandered the Sierra Madre esteem it greatly. People who have not been here deny that it is true. One person told me that while it might be true of a few psychopathic individuals it could not be typical of this place, this forest. The man who wrote the story is named J. P. S. Brown and I do not doubt a word of his story. Nor do any dogs I have met. I think the way we feel about the story tells us the way we feel about the place. To accept it is finally to leave the roadway and go off into the trees. When I lived in the forest I spent over a hundred dollars to cure a street dog named Guera, or Blondie. She was an ugly dog with one ear almost chewed off, half her teeth gone, scars from a time when someone poured boiling water on her, and numerous parts of her hide missing from dog fights. She bit many people, and was three or four years old. People I knew made fun of me for doting on this dog, and started calling her *pero de oro,* or dog of gold. I shared their laughter and I agreed with their gentle scorn. But I could not stop buying food and medicine for the dog. We all are in the end what life has made of us.

ʊ

Butterfly-Dog
by J. P. S. Brown

Tom Coyle was receiving cattle at El Limon in the Sierra Madre of Chihuahua the first time he saw the bitch dog, Mariposa. She was keeping herself delicately aloof from a pack of hungry mongrels Manuel Anaya had brought to help with the roundup. Her thin shell of a carcass did not make much track on the campground. She could not have weighed twenty pounds. Her ribs and backbone were so visible she looked like a black and tan harp.

She watched Manuel all the time. Tom could see she loved only Manuel, although he gave her little attention. He certainly never fed her much, but then Tom figured he did not have much to give away. Manuel was skinny, too.

Mariposa lay against the cool mortar of the main building of the old, crumbling hacienda at mealtime. She watched the other dogs fight over scraps the vaqueros dropped indiscriminately on the ground around their table. She rested and licked her sore places and waited. She seemed to know when Manuel was about to give her something and she stood up and looked at him and made ready to catch it. He tossed her the remnant of a tortilla without looking at her. That was all she ever seemed to get from the man, that and the odor of the food.

Later, when Tom had a chance, he took some food to her. She took it distrustfully and made Tom feel guilty. He did not like feeding another man's dog and he did not like anyone feeding his dog. He would not want Manuel to think he was trying to make Mariposa switch loyalties. He quit worrying about it when he saw she did not think any more of him because he gave her food. She ate the scraps Tom gave her, but she looked him over carefully before she allowed herself to pick them up. She would not take them from his hand.

Tom was buying cattle from Juan Vogel. The Vogel *vaqueros* were bringing cattle from a holding pasture into the corrals of El Limon, a camp located in rough mountain and canyon country. The cattle were being branded, castrated and vaccinated for Tom. They were *corriente*, native bulls over three years old. At the end of that summer, Tom planned to drive them to the railroad and export them to the States.

Manuel and his dogs had been working outside this pasture on a general roundup of the Vogel ranch. He was finished out there now and he brought his dogs to El Limon to help bring in a remnant of cattle that had been getting away each time a drive was made. These remaining cattle were the craftiest of all the *partida* that Tom wanted to brand. They had been successfully resisting the change of ownership. They had been started toward the corrals and the knives and the branding fires with other cattle every morning, but had managed to disappear before they got to the corrals.

The *vaqueros* worked afoot in that steep, rocky, brushy country. They wore *guaraches* made of strips of tire tread tied to their feet with leather thongs. Their bare, stubby feet were tough as a horse's hooves. A man on horseback could not keep the wily cattle together in that rough country. The bulls could go too many places that a man on horseback could not go. All they had to do to escape being gathered was take a path where a horse would not have good footing, or slip into brush where a man on a horse could not follow.

The *serranos*, the men who lived and worked in the Sierra Madre, could go anyplace afoot a bull could go, and many places he could not go. They did a good job of keeping cattle once they found them, but the wiliest bulls often escaped by hiding quietly a few steps away, or by running over steep ground where they could use their strength and speed and momentum to get away.

The cattle the *vaqueros* were gathering at El Limon were practiced at getting away. They never made any mad downhill rushes on their own. They just watched for a place where two or three steps would get them out of the jurisdiction of the *vaqueros*.

Down in the camp, Tom and Manuel were waiting for the first bunch of cattle the *vaqueros* were bringing in that morning. The sun was striking the top of the hill where the cattle would first appear. The descent to the corrals from the top of the hill was steep. The *vaqueros* had to stay above the cattle and drive them down off the hill into a canyon below the corrals and then uphill again to the corrals. The drive from the top of the hill to camp was over half a mile because the cattle had to cross the canyon. The line of sight that Tom and Manuel had from the camp to the top of the hill was only half that far.

Two big, spotted bulls, the first to show on the drive, appeared in the sun at the top of the hill. They walked over the crest and started down. They ambled, rocking back and forth slowly on their front legs, barely gaining ground down the hill. They stopped before entering the shade that the morning sun had not reached. They sunned themselves and waited. They listened for the other cattle on the drive behind them. Then they turned and walked calmly together into the brush. From camp Tom could see only the fine, white brushes at the ends of their tails with the sun glowing through them. They did not move.

More cattle came over the hill, walking almost as lazily as the first two. The *vaqueros* came behind them at a trot, working hard to keep them together. A *vaquero* would drive a bull a few steps and then have to leave him to go move another. The bull would stop and wait to be driven again, hoping the *vaquero* would go far enough away and become so busy that the bull could slip away in that brush, just a few steps into a thicket, like the two spotted bulls had done.

The spotted bulls stood quietly together in the brush waiting for the drive to pass them by. They stood still and sunned themselves under cover. They were making an indolent, leisurely escape.

The *vaqueros* pushed the last of the cattle off the crest and into the shade of the descent. They passed the two spotted bulls. Manuel Anaya shouted to them and told them where they were leaving the two bulls. One man went back to them. The bulls muscled deeper into the brush and disappeared. The cattle the *vaqueros* had been driving turned back toward the sunny crest of the hill. They did not want to go to the corrals. The *vaquero* had to leave the two spotted bulls in the brush to head the cattle back off the crest.

"¡OOCHA, OOCHA, MARIPOSA!" Manuel commanded. The dog sailed to the attack, her pack of lesser dogs following. She fell into the canyon below camp, out of sight. The noise of the pack fell with her, echoing, decreasing. Then she rose like an arrow through the brush on the other side of the canyon, leaving the pack behind. She went to the *vaqueros* on the hill. The two bulls had come back in sight and were moving fast toward the top of the hill. Mariposa overtook them just as they reached the crest. She rushed to the front of them, but they charged around her, hooking their big horns at her. She got back in front of them and was snapping at their noses when they forced her on over the crest and out of sight. The pack went yapping after her.

The *vaqueros* drove the rest of the cattle into the canyon and started pressing them to climb up to the corrals. The leaders lined up the narrow trail until they could see the gate and then balked, turned back, faced downhill, and hooked at the cattle that were still trying to climb out.

The Mariposa dog and her pack came back over the top of the hill with the two spotted bulls. The bulls were now completely intimidated. They flew down the hill and dove pell-mell into the herd in the canyon, hunting friends. They were in need of consolation. Mariposa had made them want to be back in the fold. They stood and looked back at her from the safety and anonymity of the herd and heaved with the excitement she had caused in singling them out.

Mariposa and her pack got behind the herd and ran it quickly up the hill and into the corrals. She nipped heels right up to the gate. The cattle were glad to make it into the corrals and be rid of her. They turned and looked at her when she stopped at the gate. She turned away from them and walked slowly to her shade by the building to lie down and pant herself and rest.

The Mariposa helped finish the work at El Limon, then Manuel took her home. Tom Coyle saw her now and then at Trigo, the headquarters of the ranch where Manuel and his family lived. Tom always looked for her at Manuel's and if he did not see her he asked about her.

Once he rode up to Manuel's house and found him scraping an ocelot hide on a table. The dog was standing under the table watching Manuel work. Now and then she moved up to smell the edge of the hide. She would sniff it and look straight into Tom's eyes. The color, markings, and texture of the fur were unblemished. The hide belonged to a *Gato tigrillo* in his prime and would bring a good payday to Manuel. The cat was a foot and half longer from nose to tail than the dog.

Manuel told Tom the Mariposa had caught the ocelot for him and had suffered no injury in the fight. Manuel had been crossing the stream at Teguaraco when the dog jumped the cat in the brush. She ran him through the water toward Manuel and he almost collided with Manuel. She cornered him under a cliff on fine scree. He lost his footing in the scree, a phenomenon that seldom happens with any cat, and the dog caught him against the wall of the cliff and broke his back. Manuel killed him with a rock.

Mariposa watched the faces of Tom and Manuel as they talked. Then, when she had not heard her name mentioned for awhile, she lay down under the table to rest.

A year later Tom rode into José Anaya's camp at Tecoyagui with a party of hunters. José was Manuel's son. Tom had been leading the hunters through the brush in the twilight for the past half hour. He had taken them on too big a circle that day, their last day of hunting, and they had tired on him. The lamplight of the house at Tecoyagui was not a welcome sight to Tom. The lamplight meant it was too late to be arriving at Tecoyagui. José's camp was at the foot of a high trail Tom's hunters would have to ride before they made their own camp. Tom had sent their beds and provisions too far up the trail that morning. They would have to camp somewhere without beds and provision and Tom did not want to impose on José. Tom would not miss the provision. The hunters had packed too much belly comfort on the mules to suit him, but he was sorry he had exhausted them so they were stopping at Tecoyagui.

When he dismounted to open the gate into the yard at José's, Tom saw the shape of an animal hanging in the darkness from a limb of mesquite over his head. It hung absolutely still, straight down from the limb.

The hunters rode past him through the gate. Not one of them noticed the figure hanging there. Tom noticed it because it was ominously familiar, but its stillness was so absolute and it was so close by the place a man had to stand to open the gate, that he could not believe what he was seeing.

Tom ducked under it and closed the gate and then walked around it, leading his horse, so he could see it better on the side where the lamplight touched it. He saw it was a little black and tan dog hanging rigidly by a wire around its neck. The nose pointed sharply straight up the wire. The tail pointed straight down in line with the wire. All that was left of the dog now depended on a wire stretched tight in the dark, touched by lamplight, at the bottom of a canyon in the Sierra Madre. Not a breeze stirred it.

Tom led his horse to the house. The hunters were lowering themselves stiffly from their saddles. Tom decided they would have to stay the night here.

José Anaya came smiling to him.

"Come in to the coffee, Tomás," José said. "Tell your friends."

"How is it with you, José?" Tom asked.

"*Mucho piojo*. Much lice. Much ruin," José said, smiling, and he made the gesture of cracking a louse between his thumbnails. That meant he was suffering hard times. "But we'll make it unless the rains are late again. We've lost many cattle from hunger and drouth, though."

"We saw no game either. Not even a track. *Menos mal*. Let the poor things live, if they can."

José handed Tom a cup of black coffee. Tom wondered how many times José's woman had reboiled the grounds. It was a big sacrifice for his family to give away coffee. Tom would be leading the hunters out of the Sierra the next day. The grouchy hunters were headed back to their land of plenty without having killed anything in the Sierra Madre. He would lighten the packs on the mules and send some famously advertised canned goods back to José. He would appreciate them more than anyone in North America, even though he had certainly never heard their famous names.

Tom squatted on his heels and sipped his coffee. José began unsaddling his horse for him. "You will stay the night, won't you?" José asked gently. "You have to. These men can't ride that bad trail. The night is too dark for anyone to travel now."

José laid Tom's saddle down on its side, slipped the bridle onto the horse's neck so he could eat, and poured him a measure of corn on the ground.

"What happened to the dog?" Tom asked.

"We caught her in the provisions."

Tom said nothing.

"She was a good dog," José said.

Tom sipped his coffee.

"You remember my father's dog, the Mariposa?"

Tom could not answer. Be careful, he thought. Keep your *gringo* mouth shut. He knows how much you liked her. Still, why in the hell? That good little dog.

"She alighted on the wrong flower," José said. He tried to smile, as if for the pleasure of a small joke between friends.

Alamos, Sonora, with the Church of the Purisma Concepción and palacios lining the Plaza.

Pool hall on the Alameda in Alamos.

Opposite: Lechuguilla

*Mother and daughters
outside their home in
Aguas Calientes.*

*Opposite: Flowering
nesco and hecho cactus.*

Peaks of the Sierra
Alamos rise above bare
trees and organ-pipe
cactus.

*Mother and daughters
with parasols against a
wall bordered with
bougainvillea.*

Alamos

Aguas Calientes

Above and opposite:
El Día de los Muertos
in Alamos.

Teodoro Zasueta Corral

THREE

The Feel of the Life

THERE IS A FEEL OF RAIN in the cool December air. It is the day of the Virgin of Conception and squads of young girls in long white dresses trek to the church for their confirmation. In a few days it will be the day of the Virgin of Guadalupe. And then will begin Advent and the posadas, the processions from house to house that recall the search by Mary and Joseph for shelter. And then the New Year. Las equipatas must begin soon, surely they must. And then . . . .

This year las aguas were very strong and continued longer into the fall than was normal. For this reason, the hills are still semiclad in green, though the inevitable cannot be avoided. The strong summer rains have ceased and each day now more leaves come down. The Sonoran morning-glory tree is bare but in flower. When Howard Scott Gentry compiled his taxonomic descriptions of the forest, this particular tree, called palo santo by the Mexicans, drove him past the neutral language of science and into song: "A spectacular tree . . . with smooth, white-gray bark like the hide of a hippopotamus. It flowers in winter when leafless, holding a high, thin spread of white corollas like stars against the morning sky. The stars soon fall upon the ground, where the deer eat them." Also, the first amapas are coming on here and there. The kapok that bloomed last spring, then went to fruit, now is bare except for large pods hanging from the tips of the limbs. Some of the pods have opened and huge white bolls of fiber are suspended like globes of snow. Once, they were gathered and became the stuffing for pillows, mattresses and the like. Then the world moved on to synthetic fibers and now the tree goes through its cycle largely undisturbed by the appetites of our kind.

We load up the truck for a day in the campo. Two local Mexicanos come with us. They are the *maestros* of the forest, we the doltish students. In part, we are idly checking on places described by John Hilton and Howard Scott Gentry decades ago. But in the main, we are wandering without intention. Just outside of Alamos, the cobbles end and the world of dirt caminos begins. Soon we are at the Cuchujaqui, the river quiet and lined with sabinos. Nearby, tucked away in a side arroyo a giant fig, with its canopy a hundred or more feet in radius, dominates its quiet corner of the world. Tiger billed herons, trogons, kingfishers and other birds hunt food along the edges of the río. Sometimes the mot-mot is also found here. Across the stream on the hillside lie the trunks of amapas, torotes, and other trees, all felled in the last week or two as the inexorable march of buffel grass planting goes on. A kind of death lingers here in the air.

We wade over on a rock bed for trucks, climb up and for a while move through the forest at an astounding twenty-five miles an hour. Then we take a fork and stream toward the Sierra Madre and our speed falls away. Soon a village appears, Mezquital, a recently launched community of Mayos. It is very still. The houses are mud and wattle-and-daub, the yards bare dirt swept immaculately. By the road are two small heaps of stone covered with paper flowers and small candles. Pigs running freely barely look up as we pass and a tom turkey fans his tail at us.

We stop often on the dirt track as Yermo and Saul point out a tree in bloom, the vanishing form of a bird disappearing into the forest, the striking plants clinging to a cliff. For them, each plant has a name that speaks of a use or of a warning. Each square foot has the imprint of man because someone uses that ground, or lived in that ground, or died on that ground, or haunts that ground. At La Labor we admire an ancient hacienda, at the fork to El Tepeguaje, they speak warmly of the fiesta held there each February. Finally we reach El Sabino and El Cajón, two villages sharing a stream lined with cypresses. We stop at a house where a group of men watch a neighbor fashion furniture with a machete. The houses are all white-washed, and on the roofs, which are often thatch from the local palms, melons and hay and other provisions are stored beyond the reach of livestock, dogs, and coyotes. One of the men watching the work decides to come with us and guide us and visit friends. We pass through Guirocoba, a town noted by locals for its strain of blue-eyed Mexicans, the result of two Americans who were disenchanted with World War I, came here, and stuck. Then we take a rocky track between some cerros (ridges) and drop down to Agua Caliente.

It is mid-day Sunday as we roll slowly, very slowly in. The women of the village are busy chopping weeds, and raking. Every square foot of the village has been swept by women wielding the fronds of palms and the dirt bears the marks of this scratching. The men of the village seem to watch this activity and listen to music from battery powered cassette players. Each house is fenced with brasil *(Haematoxylon brasiletto),* a wood of the campo that is famous for burning when green and with a greenish flame. The trunks are deeply braided and look like a column of serpents. The wood is also used for making a light-red dye and the carving of rosaries.

We walk down toward the arroyo running below the houses. Hot water bubbles up from the ground and trails away leaving a vivid green smear of algae in its wake. A young girl kneels by one pool of hot water pounding

clothes clean on a rock. It is very quiet, the stillness of a day of rest, or of
work not done earlier in the week. Mules, burros, and chickens wander
about us and the village lacks roads, as it largely lacks trucks, and is laced
together by footpaths. Each house seems to explode with bouganvilleas or
other shrubs and the effect is not of the dirt or the thatch or the largely
leafless hills, but of color, violent, primary colors.

Leaning against a fence is a young woman, still in her teens. She holds a
baby and the swelling in her belly suggests she is again with child. Behind her
on the porch, a thicket of plants grows from tin cans hung on the white-
washed wall. Her face is very serene, the skin smooth. She is a recruit in an
enormous army devouring the natural world, a statistic in a demographic
catastrophe often called the population explosion. Or at least that is how it is
described when the person in question is poor. In the industrial nations, it is
called development and progress. On the ground it always looks much the
same—a taking of materials by human beings at a rate that many doubt the
earth can endure. No doubt there is much merit in these characterizations. In
the spring, she will probably be the mother of two children and I do not
know how she will describe this fact. It is all much easier to judge when one
is not standing by a fence, listening to a baby and looking into a young
mother's eyes. Just as it is much easier to dismiss the idea of onzas back in
the laboratory than when one is a guest under a man's ramada and one
listens to the people of the campo describe close encounters with this phan-
tom of the forest.

After a while we retrace our tracks to Guirocoba and then strike north on
a path that is more maintained by burros than machines. Soon the ground
rises, the sides of a canyon pinch in, and we climb into oaks studded with
palms. Orchids begin to appear on the trees, the air grows cool with a
refreshing dampness, and there is more shade than light. We are going to
Choquincahui, an old mining site perched high on the cerro. In his writings
Hilton mentions finding palma de la Virgen *(Dioon purpusii)* somewhere
above us and we have never seen the plant outside of a garden in town. The
palma is a cycad, one of the most ancient of plant forms. In Guirocoba,
Gentry discovered half a century ago that people made a paste from the seed
for curing maladies of the eye.

Finally, the road peters out and only a burro track remains. High up on a
hill, we see the thatched huts of a family, and walk toward it. Lying along
the path, one on each side, are two heaps of stones, each with a cross. The
rocks remember two brothers killed three years ago. They are not buried
here. The shrines simply mark where they fell. Their names and ages are
carved into the wood, which has already aged to a fine silver. The crosses are
beginning to tilt and the mounds are covered with paper wreaths from the

Day of the Dead. One brother was thirty-eight years old. I am told the story of their deaths. Later, I am told another story by people who were there at the time. No doubt there are yet more stories, none of which will quite agree with each other. In the campo, history is a living force and yet it is a plastic thing subject to change, enhancement, addition, and subtraction. It is not simply a matter of establishing the facts and setting the record straight for this thing we call history. It is more that the past continues to rub up against the present in a kind of conversation and as this talk continues both the past and the present evolve and offer up new ideas and meanings.

The men of the casa sit on the porch, their saddles hanging from the vigas over their heads. They bring forth a wooden bench, the legs stout forks cut from a tree, and invite us to join them. It is Sunday, as I have said, and work is briefly forgotten in the campo. We ask of the palm of the Virgin and if it truly grows in this area. Yes, the father says, it is very nearby. He will show us. As he speaks, children watch as shy as deer and yet are unable to look away from the strangers. Clean clothes dry on the fence but the woman of the house never comes out from her kitchen.

The way to the palms of the Virgin entails an almost vertical drop down into the neighboring arroyo and then a steep climb up to the man's milpa of corn. We cross the poles barring stock from his field and then climb yet more. The field is almost straight up and down. His son scampers ahead with ease. And then two-thirds of the way up, we find them. Small, palmlike plants nestled amid the dry stalks of the corn. Larger palms, like the cycads with trunks blackened from fire, stud the hillside. To prepare this field the man felled the forest with his axe and machete. Then he burned it. It will serve his family for two or three years and then the fertility will be sucked from the soil and he will abandon it to the forest for ten or twenty years. The trees will return, thrive, and be felled yet again. This has happened many times and the face of the forest is in part shaped by this practice. Perhaps, his father once fired this same slope. Perhaps, his sons or grandsons will fell it yet again.

So we find the cycads, the ancestors of much that now carpets the earth. They are a foot or two high, the fronds a rich, waxy green, the small stubby trunks charred by the fire of man. They grow in the wild, only the wild here is a field of corn.

On the way back, we suddenly brake to a stop as Yermo and Saul point out a flock of parrots perched on a tree, the green of their feathers electric against the bare limbs. Finally, the birds bolt and fly away chattering into the selva, saying things to themselves I do not understand.

❖

The faces pass by on the trail, and disappear again and what they think we can only guess. They avoid the authorities, distrust the towns, write no books, fail to make a page in the histories. Their small houses dot the forest, cling to the slopes of the sierra, show up in impossible canyons. Government talks about them but not to them. They are the campesinos and they seem to always outlast everyone else.

The man was sitting high on the top of a cliff in the Sierra Madre Occidental of Mexico in the dark shade of an *aliso* tree. He had been waiting for afternoon shade to cover the face of the cliff so he could climb down and pluck an *enjambre,* a wild beehive, from the face. The time was spring and the hives were full of honey, though the Sierra was dry . . . . He felt akin to all who made their living in the Sierra. *Tienen derecho,* they have a right to do what they do, he felt.

The man was tall and wiry. He was strong. He tied tire treads on the soles of his feet with leather thongs that cost him more than he could afford. These *huaraches* were all the protection he had ever used or needed for getting from one place to another . . . . Few people in the world knew him. He did not care or worry about being known by anyone. He was a calm man who waited, watched, and hoped for dark, high heavy clouds to come, day or night, early or late, with rain. He was a man who was a friend of lightning, friend of the torrent or the flood, and an enemy of death. He was friend to beasts and growing corn. He was enemy to hunger, cruelty, devastation, wasted fat, oil, and wood, to raucous women and wooing . . . .

J.P.S. Brown, *The Forests of the Night*
(New York: Dial Press, 1974), 4–5.

There is no way to avoid meeting people and they are seldom what they seem at first. They stop and talk and immediately their life story, their dreams, their class, their past and future are filled in, filed, and dismissed. And then, a kind of friendship occurs and it turns out there is more going on than first imagined. The otherness of a different culture seems not so different after all. And the similarities that all people share, well, these things also turn out to be not enough to make everyone the same, or every nation.

We are trained to keep things separate. Human history must stay out of natural history, and science must be kept safe from poetry and often we insist on seeing the individual species of trees and damn the forest. In some ways, the work of Howard Scott Gentry in the 1930s, when he compiled *Río Mayo Plants,* is a monument to this drive. A half century later his work is the bedrock of botanical understanding in this area. But Gentry was too alert and too alive to keep a single focus and things besides the taxonomy of the forest continually spill into his writings. He never let his love of plants blind him to his love of life. Nor should anyone else who wishes truly to savor the elements that lurk in that single English word, *place.*

> Trails also lead to the stream side where women wash clothes with loud flapping and beating upon the rocks. There everybody bathes, infrequently, but almost invariably on San Juan's Day, which falls the twenty-fourth of June and about the day the very welcome summer rains begin. "Of all the fiesta days," my *mozo,* Juanito, said, "San Bernardans like best the day of San Juan. At the first suggestion of dawn the father rouses his household and they all go down to the arroyo to bathe. Later they return to the house and gorge upon watermelons, the fruit they love. These have been raised by irrigation in the little arroyo side gardens during the hot spring dry season. They put up gay paper decorations; visit one another's houses and in the evening dance and sing. It is the day for the beginning of *Las Aguas* when the verdant summer growing season begins."

> Howard Scott Gentry, "Caminos of San Bernardo,"
> *The Michigan Alumnus Quarterly Review* (Winter, 1942).

Besides the life, there is the death, a basic part of the life. Everything dies just as everything lives. But facing these facts or avoiding these facts is the hard kernel of strategies we hide inside our cultures. The Mexicans are notorious for facing death. And then, once a year, they have a Day of the Dead and wallow in the yawning graves that greet every tingling cell on the planet.

> It is significant that a country as sorrowful as ours should have so many and such joyous fiestas. Their frequency, their brilliance and excitement, the enthusiasm with which we take part, all suggest that without them we would explode . . . . The word death is not pronounced in New York, in Paris, in London, because it burns the lips. The Mexican, in contrast, celebrates it; it is one of his favorite toys and his most steadfast love. True, there is perhaps as much fear in his attitude as in that of others, but at least death is not hidden away.

> Octavio Paz, *Labyrinth of Solitude: Life and Thought in Mexico,*
> trans. Lysander Kemp (London: Penquin Press, 1967).

❖

BOWDEN

The town is ready for the night. The dress has come from Tijuana and costs six hundred dollars. The band has been hired, the cattlemen's hall rented. Vendors of tacos, elotes, exquisitos, and chicharrones line the street in front of the building. There are fifteen sons and daughters and very little money. The old man works for twenty-two dollars a week, his son shovels cement and makes ten dollars a day, and so forth. But this is different, this is the wedding, the youngest daughter is being married, and a celebration is in order.

The family rises to the occasion. The old man with fifteen sons and daughters cries at the ceremony. He is wearing new bedroom slippers instead of his usual huaraches. And then the event shifts into another gear. Hundreds stream into the reception, the bride enters with her maids, and the band strikes up a number that sounds like the bump and grind of a burlesque hall. The maid of honor wears a black dress with a plunging neckline, a large black hat, and dark eyes that say yes, yes, yes. She never smiles, she hardly can. After all, she is a goddess tonight. One glance from her could break a man's heart, grind up his bones to dust, destroy his dreams, and leave him a spent shell empty of blood. The men are dressed in their very best jeans, their best belts, their cleanest shirts, and all wear polished boots. The young women are shimmering clouds of satin, their faces masks. It will take hours and hours. By the early morning, the drinking will have taken hold and there will be a few fights. The dancing, well, the dancing will say what is on everyone's mind. Everyone will want to touch someone else, to be held, to hold, to taste, dream, believe. We will all be as helpless as insects before a blooming flower, drawn in further and further. Don't tell me about the senseless waste of money on this fiesta. Shut up about demographics, over-population, infant mortality, malnutrition, death, dying, doom. No one here, thank God, will listen. See those lips, hear that beat. The breast swells, the child hungers for the milk, the night wraps around like velvet.

No one is poor tonight. No one at midnight fears the morning. No one doubts anything. Perhaps, no one thinks. Can we truly be that lucky? At times it is impossible to grasp fully the poverty of the people of the forest. And at times it is impossible to believe in the poverty of the people of the forest. Of course, nothing that is happening tonight is new. I am grateful for that fact. This is now, tomorrow, the day after. It is in the blood. But we often forget that fact, forget the blood. We forget the deeper promptings that make us what we truly are. And that is when we are truly poor.

We live at a time when we chafe at the restraints that our minds and our customs and our glimpses of the future have imposed upon us. We cannot imagine any longer a situation that does not call for rules, often new rules. We have created a culture where even the idea of wilderness is encapsulated within regulations, permits, and strict decorum. Perhaps there is nothing to be done about these facts. Still, deeper impulses linger and whisper to us acts of rebellion.

❖

The *metate* lies by my foot, a dark, rock slab busted in half. There are pieces of pottery, worked edges of stone—over there is a *mano*. All around me is scattered the debris of an earlier people, the stamp of an earlier time. I am with a friend down by the Río Cuchujaqui and this is his land, his *rancho*. For an hour we have hopped on boulders across streams, waded under giant sabinos, watched butterflies flutter past our eyes. In town, he is a reserved man, a serious man given to business. In town, he always speaks very carefully, as befits a man of his position. He is in his forties, his town house is splendid, and often he sits there watching the Los Angeles Dodgers play, the image sucked down from the heavens by his satellite dish. But out here, he bounds about like a child, with huaraches on his feet, and every time I touch a plant he instantly supplies a name, tells of a use. It is almost like he is introducing me to old friends.

He asks if I want the metate. Ah, the taking, the collecting, that demon deep within me, within us all. We must take to prove we have been there. We loot to assure ourselves it has all happened, to show others where we have gone and who we have been. I am tempted, but I say no. On my patio, the metate will be a stone. In time, I will forget exactly where I found it. And then in more time, I will forget that I even have it. Here it is still whispers of a world.

I am learning, slowly to be sure, but I am learning. My friend is part of what many consider the problem. His land by the river, it is not what we call natural. There is very little understory because his cattle eat it. They devour the homes of insects, the sanctuaries of birds. They befoul the waters that shelter endangered species of fish. They live off his land. And these steers are so damn tame. They come up to us out of the forest like dogs, pushing their heads toward us. He smiles, and explains that they want salt, that usually he carries salt for them and they eat it from his hand. They also munch down all those plants he keeps telling me about, those plants that make a dye, or cure a bad stomach, or fight a cold. He points and plucks up what looks to me like an undistinguished weed. This plant, he says, is excellent for clearing the sinuses, but only the young growing tips, he laughs. Take too much, he warns, and it can make you very ill, it can kill you. How did he learn the proper amount for a cure, I ask. Oh, he says, from his mother.

Besides this constant feeding by his cattle on the forest, he cuts large swatches of the trees down for planting the buffel grass, that South African import. The grass lingers, he says, for about ten years and then its energy is spent, the land must be butchered again, and new seed cast. From this effort comes calves and they are shipped to the United States and go to feedlots. There they eat grain for a short while, and then they go to the slaughter house and onto my table.

Against these simple economic facts, there are the butterflies. Yesterday, some friends of mine who are experts in these matters identified fifty-six species in one February day. When they told me this, I felt like a blind man. I could at most notice a half dozen, some white ones, some yellow ones, a black one, some orange ones. But fifty-six? Obviously, I do not know what is going on around me. The butterfly experts told me that in the summer after the rains, they could probably find ninety species in a day.

As I look down at the metate with my friend, a zebra butterfly floats by, its big wings black and yellow. They tend to fly in groups in a kind of single file, each one following the leader. Two things about them are unknown. No one has figured out if the leadership of the flight changes. And no one knows why they follow each other. Well, I can feel some sympathy for them. I am barging about the forest, following a whole bunch of leaders, and I'm not sure why and I'm not sure who exactly gets to be the leader. My first impulse in this place is to save it. I am stuffed with phrases like endangered species, ecosystems, balance of nature, carrying capacity, and the like. And I've got facts and figures to back up all this babble. When I fly over this forest, I see impending ruin. Big chunks are missing. Peasants on the *ejidos* slaughter everything. Ranchers, like my friend, consult experts, and then take huge patches. Up higher in the sierra, international banks finance a lumber industry that obliterates ancient forests. This is like every other place on a planet of about six billion human beings.

I say none of this to my friend. I doubt it would be news to him. We walk on, cross a small river, cut under a big fig tree, and climb up a hill. I ask him, as we stumble on, if those younger than himself, if the generation growing up, will know the plants as he does, know the uses and methods of the forest like he does. "No," he says, with no apparent problem, "they will learn other things. Perhaps, better things."

Then we reach the bench above the river. Here he has built a jacal, a thatched-roof ramada without walls. He tells me that he comes out here to think. He pauses and says, "If I lose everything, I could still come out here to this land and I could survive." I know he means it. When he was a child, he used to walk thirty-seven miles into town. His village was against the sierra and Tarahumara Indians would come down to trade. I have been to his native village and it is still a place a couple of centuries away from his satellite dish and house in town. I sit under his jacal and drink a cold beer. I hear his voice saying that here he could survive. I believe him and I know that left to the same ground I would die, my stomach growling from its exquisite diet of ecological truisms.

I have no answers and for that I am grateful. The answers, I know, belong to the past. They are very tired answers about leaving nothing but my footprints, about not making fires, never leaving litter, never straying from marked trails, and carefully burying my feces. Answers that say pack everything out, and stay in designated camping areas. They are answers of pure mind and tell me nothing in this forest of the flesh. The future, if there is to be one, must find new answers. Maybe the beer helps. As we sit there and listen to the flies buzz, I ask him if he sees many deer. While we were walking, I saw some fresh tracks in the sand by the river. He slowly smiles and tells me that a couple of Indians look after his ranch and they shoot everything they see. And then he says, I can come out anytime I want and camp here. I thank him. Because I would rather be here than in a national park. When I listen closely, I can hear past the flies buzzing and what I catch is a faint cry of the future. A place where if there is to be a forest, we will be in it. All we get to decide is if our presence is for better or worse.

Of course, there are other days. Sometimes I climb high into the sierra and go up canyons where the cows cannot follow. The way will be blocked by huge boulders, cliffs, hard scrambles where I fear falling. I find pristine waterfalls splashing into deep, clear pools, orchids clinging to rocks within easy reach of my hand. On the cliff above, amapas bloom and rare cacti obstinately make a home. I climb up on a huge boulder and find *Echinocereus gentryi,* a species Howard Scott Gentry first discovered in the thirties and one I have never found growing in the wild before. I become wildly excited and then I look over and see other specimens growing on a cliff, strands of it two- or three-feet-long hanging down like spaghetti as thick as my fingers. A hummingbird roars past my head, magpie jays cry out and watch me from a tree, and God, I want nothing here ever to change, not a leaf or a pebble. I want the place declared an international treasure and after I leave it today, I will blow up the mouth of the canyon, hiding it forever the way the early Jesuit fathers are rumored to have hidden their precious (and mythical) gold and silver mines. I will keep this place safe from, from . . . from what?

From my mouth, from my teeth, from my alimentary canal? From all the others just like me who would like to be here? From the six billion of my own species? From the guy I know in town who collects odd plants and sells them to Americans? From the scientists who will insist on collecting something or the other? From the fireplace where I like to sit with a glass of wine in the evening and watch the flames lick the wood of the forest? From the photographers who will follow my footsteps and spend hundreds of dollars on film and on chemical processing in order to capture these precious moments of that thing we call wilderness? From the all but extinct wolf that is no longer at my door?

A while back I was having a drink on the roof of a restaurant in a small town further south in this same forest. It is a town almost no one goes to, a colonial town that time and tourism has forgotten. In the narrow cobblestone street below, a funeral procession filed past with a couple of hundred people dressed in black and on foot following the coffin to the campo santo on the edge of town. Another American suddenly came out onto the roof—ah, no place is far enough!—and we drank and talked. He said he was from California and one day he read a book and it changed his life. The book said that if one were willing to live on fifty to seventy-five dollars a day, one could live anywhere in the Third World. So he was looking, and had just driven into this isolated town. I swallowed my glass of wine, and did a quick computation in my head, and thought, my God, he's trying to pare his life down to between eighteen and twenty-seven thousand dollars a year. Most of the people I know in the forest make, if they are lucky, five bucks a day and the truly lucky ones make say ten dollars a day. From this they fabricate a world, complete with love, failure, birth, and death. There is a good deal of music also. And they eat everything they can find.

I mean eat it. Once a friend of mine was driving in the forest and found a man walking with a dead coati mundi (a raccoon-like animal) dangling from one hand. My friend stopped and asked the man what he was going to do with it. He said the meat was very good for tacos. So I listened to the American describe his new frugal future with a good deal of scorn, the cheap kind of scorn we all gleefully indulge in. But I was no different than he was. It takes a king's ransom just to keep me rolling in the manner to which I have become accustomed. When I am sitting in my secret canyon with the rare cacti and the orchids and the pure pools under the waterfalls, I look at birds through binoculars that cost three hundred dollars. I pull them from my two-hundred–dollar backpack. And so forth. I can't say that I feel guilty about spending this kind of money. Like everybody I know, I figure I am just getting by, walking lightly, and barely making it. And I am not likely to change of my own volition any more than the people I know in the forest are going to change of their own volition.

We need new answers and our old answers only get in the way. They are like those Sabbath values nineteenth-century writers like Mark Twain always made fun of—pieties we tell others but that we make sure do not confine our own lives and habits. We've got a pantry full of junked words like progress, development, capitalism, communism, industrialism, and environmentalism and, if we really get desperate, we haul out that old favorite, lifestyle. We prefer this rhetoric to facing a rather simple problem: In a world where almost everyone is poor, our species takes things faster than they are replaced. And whether one heads into the forest with a machete or a two-hundred–dollar backpack, this simple fact does not change.

Always, I leave my secret canyon and descend back into my comforts. I come down the mountain on a trail carved deep into the rock by centuries of burros going to and fro. I walk under huge trees, carefully skirt giant cacti, catch now and then the flash of orioles in the canopy of green, and once in a while see a trogon. The sound of rushing water always makes my heart light, and when I get lower I take pleasure in the small corn fields and stone walls that chew small bits of the forest. I look at them and smell fresh tortillas hot off the *comal*. I go past the shrine to the Virgin, negotiate with cows coming up the trail, and finally cross a stream and come out at a small public park on the edge of town. It is usually by then afternoon and the heat is on.

One day I find a couple camping in a van. They hail me, and offer a cold beer. They have been in town, they say, for two days and not yet left this small patch against the mountain, have not yet even ventured the half mile or so to the plaza. The man is in his sixties, the woman younger. They came in during the night, they say, and are looking for a place to live in Mexico. As they drove up the rutted dirt road to the park in the night, they tell me, suddenly a Mexican man dressed in a white sheet stood before their headlights with a huge flagon of beer. He invited them to his house for a drink and then took them to the campsite. They had brought clams from the coast and they gave them to him. As I drain my beer and listen, their story begins to leap and bound and lose the annoying logic that we so depend upon. The next morning, they continue, they met a man who lives in a small house near the park. He had just had six teeth extracted and invited them to park at his place. Then he consulted with his daughters, and offered them free a small hut down the road as a home for a few weeks while they looked for a permanent house. They went to inspect it and as they stood in the back yard the man they had met that first night came to the patio wall of the adjoining house, and handed over a platter of *paella*, a rice dish he had made from their clams. A feeling of magic to be sure. They were moving in that afternoon.

The Mexican man who has had six teeth just extracted comes over with one of his daughters and we exchange greetings. I am very tired from my hike. My head is full of rare cacti, plump orchids, a platter of food handed over the wall, the clatter of first worlds, second worlds, third worlds. The heat is on and the cold beer tastes very good.

Later I realize I have missed what is right before my eyes. The man who finds the American couple a free house, he owns no house. He is in his forties and he has never for a single instant owned a square foot of this earth. I learn this fact in a rather simple way: One morning I get up, and just down the road find that two hundred of the desperately poor families in town have seized and occupied twenty idle acres that happen to be owned by a Mexican friend of mine. The man with the six extracted teeth is one of the soldiers in this invasion. Then I learn that my neighbor two doors down, a school-teacher, is one of the leaders of this land seizure—he too has never owned a house or a patch of dirt. The families that move onto the land throw up a few jacales made of sticks and plastic garbage bags, wield machetes, and seemingly overnight clear the ground of brush. Then they divide it all up into lots, each twenty-five meters by fifteen meters. The government hesitates, then agrees to buy the land from my friend and sell it with long term mort-gages to the families. Such an expropriation by the poor has never happened in the town before, at least not since the bloody revolution between 1910 and 1920.

I go with my schoolteacher neighbor to the land for the big day, the day the lots are assigned by a drawing. There are 153 lots and these are not enough for all the poor who want a home. They stand under a ramada on the cleared land around a battered kitchen table with a huge hole in it. A glass gallon jar with folded pieces of paper rests on the table top. It is 11 A.M. and the heat and stillness of the day have fallen with weight on everyone's shoulders. People press in closely, the men hiding their nervousness behind their passive faces, the women willing to be more openly anxious, some even smoking in public. Many of the people are short and dark.

A name is called and a man steps forward, reaches into the jar, pulls a slip, hands it to a clerk, and his lot is recorded. Sometimes the new owner can sign his name, sometimes he cannot. One old woman can make no sense of the slip she pulls out of the jar because she has never learned how to read numbers. As each person draws his lot, there is a light flutter of applause and smiles here and there. I follow the new owners out into the field as they search for their future homes in the maze of little plots. The men, when they find their lots, instantly check the boundary stakes. The women tend to stand in the center of their lots and smile. Some skip and dance. I see the man who befriended the American couple on the very day he had six teeth pulled. He looks over at me, gives a quick smile and a thumbs up, and strides on with his son to find his lot. I talk with another man who is twenty-six years old and has a wife and two children. He has never had his own home before. His work? Ah, he does a little of this and that he says. He pauses and explains that he also hunts deer in the sierra. And then he starts checking the bound-ary markers of his new, tiny domain.

I have never seen such a ferocity for a patch of earth in my life. Nor have I ever witnessed such pleasure as the people displayed that day. It was quiet pleasure, one made up of very slow movements and soft almost velvetlike gestures. We can never save the forest if we ignore that hunger. Nor can we ever save the forest or ourselves if we let our hungers consume everything and justify everything.

What we want, always and everywhere it seems, is a program, a list of absolute and clear rules, a manual of procedures. And what we get are contradictions, forces, feelings pouring from deep wells we cannot even admit to very often. This time no engineers will be able to help with cold plans of dams, aqueducts, and tables of figures. The engineers have already had their fun with us and their clear simple blueprints have not solved the problem. The work, I suspect, will be done on the ground, in the forest, with machetes, computers, weddings, burials, steers, butterflies, and now and then a backpack. It will be a faltering kind of work, a groping without good light. We will try this, we will try that, we will hesitate, and then plunge on ahead. Often, we will make up things as we go along. It will not be a bad experience but it will be an experience that lacks the sense of certainty that has comforted us in the past and blinded us in the past.

At times, we will sit under a kapok tree, and watch the fluff from its pods blow away in the wind. A small green frog will boom out its lust with the first rains and by our feet a trail of mochomos will march past carrying loot stripped from a tree overnight. The shadow of a hawk will cross our faces and we will not fear.

❖

FOUR

Vaya Con Dios

THE FIRST MAN WAS CALLED HEAD OF A COW, Cabeza de Vaca. He and three companions walked six thousand miles, beginning around Galveston, Texas, and blundered into the place we now call the Southwest in the United States, the Northwest in Mexico. Since then of course, many have followed in his footsteps as explorers, settlers, prospectors, missionaries, conquistadors, vagabonds, scientists, and tourists. I doubt that any person has ever penetrated the country as deeply as Cabeza de Vaca and I wonder if anyone ever will. The blood price for such a journey is high, very high.

While many people are said to have conquered America, Cabeza de Vaca was conquered by America. He began with different intentions. His grandfather had taken the Canary Islands, enslaved the native people, and set his stamp upon that land. Cabeza de Vaca was raised in a household staffed with slaves from this sacking. When he arrived in this New World, he was the second in command of an expedition to seize Florida, find gold, spawn empire. The men starved, and became lost and in time, their number was pared from several hundred to finally four souls huddled on the Texas coast. By this time they wore no clothes, had been the slaves of Indians, had learned the languages, and knew how to survive off the land. They had been slowly stripped of the Old World that adorned their bodies and much of their souls. They were three Spaniards and a Moor from the coast of Morocco and they began to walk toward Mexico.

The cold they did not feel, nor hunger either. And to the native Americans they met along the way they seemed like holy men, like healers. They were reluctant to try and effect cures. One of their number felt he was not clean enough, not free of sin enough to have such powers. But the people they met insisted and so they tried, and many were healed. Soon they traveled with hundreds in their entourage, with entire villages giving them food and shelter and objects of power—arrowheads made of turquoise, magic gourds, special pelts, copper bells. The four companions walked naked at the head of this procession, walked across Texas, walked across southern New Mexico, walked across southeastern Arizona, dove into Sonora.

They escape time. We are fated to live almost every moment of our lives in the future tense, in anticipation of things we will do, things we will achieve, people we will become. The past for us is a vast barren that pulls at us from behind, a place we know by reputation. But we do not live there. The present, it hardly exists, the briefest flickering as we stride ahead, our minds focused on our becoming, becoming, becoming. But the future, it justifies all our acts, occupies all our days and nights, and feeds all our lusts. We will be.

Cabeza de Vaca escaped into the present in his six thousand miles of trudging, in his years on the trail. He became perhaps the only one of our number ever truly to live in America. His world became bizarre yet normal. In central Sonora, natives offered him six hundred deer hearts. Of course, he shared this bounty with everyone. He and his companions always shared. And so while they kept plunging on toward their Mexico, two things happened. One, they were always exactly wherever they were, healing, sharing food, talking, and learning from the Indians. And they were remade from whatever they were into something that had probably never been before: people from the Old World who have been devoured by the New World.

Finally, in northern Sinaloa, they came upon Spaniards. Their compatriots did not recognize these naked men at the head of a column of natives as their fellow citizens. The Spaniards were slavers, and had devastated and depopulated much of Sonora. They wished to make Cabeza de Vaca's entourage into slaves, also. They envied his friendship with the natives and their respect for him. Cabeza de Vaca forbade the slavers to act and denounced their activities. The Spaniards argued. They tried to convince the Indians that the four men they were following were just like themselves and not special or different men. The Indians rejected this argument out of hand.

> The Indians paid no attention to this . . . . They replied that the Christians lied: We had come from the sunrise, they from the sunset; we healed the sick, they killed the sound; we came naked and barefoot, they clothed, horsed, and lanced; we coveted nothing but gave whatever we were given, while they robbed whomever they found and bestowed nothing on anyone.

> Alvar Núñez Cabeza de Vaca,
> *Adventures in the Unknown Interior of America* (1542).

Of course, these moments passed. When the four men arrived in Culiacan, they still found clothes unbearable to wear and Cabeza de Vaca preferred the ground to a soft bed. By the time, in the summer of 1536, he arrived in Mexico he was wardrobed by Hernán Cortés, the great conqueror. And from his lips escaped stories that became the seven cities of gold, and launched the greed that became the Coronado expedition of 1540. The man conquered by America slowly freed himself, and became again a Spaniard with a sword. But not quite. He was later sent to South America, led an expedition into

Paraguay, and was returned to Spain and prison for basically being too kind to Indians.

We are left with his brief book, *Adventures in the Unknown Interior of America,* the first and best book ever written on the place that still has no common name, that dry hot region called Southwest or Northwest depending on a person's national background. His little yet profound book ends in the tropical forest that blankets southern Sonora and rolls on into Sinaloa, a place described by Cabeza de Vaca as "no doubt, the most prolific land in all these Indies. It produces three crops a year; the trees bear a great variety of fruit; and beautiful rivers and brimming springs abound throughout. . . . This land, in short, lacks nothing to be regarded as blest."

We look again, our eyes weary with centuries of life here, our hearts heavy with centuries of plundering. We have fabricated a world so dense with objects and demands that we need national parks and official wildernesses as sanctuaries from its fangs and talons. We tell each other at times that we have lost touch with something that truly is life. We spend most of our time on tomorrow and hardly notice today. We look into the forest and wonder what might be there. We hesitate.

A faint memory tugs.

Yes.

❖

Christina's world is different than we remember it from the Andrew Wyeth painting. She has no limp this time and she is not crawling toward the big house with yearning radiating from her limbs. Instead, she rises at three A. M. and grinds corn on the metate for tortillas. The black stone is embedded in her *cocina* right next to the wood fire where small limbs from the forest crackle in the hours before light. Her face is round, the teeth perfect and white, the smile seeming to come without effort. Her five children still sleep, as does her husband. They will arise when the tortillas are made and the coffee bubbles over the flames. She is a woman and she is about her work in the hours before the sun touches the sierra and the world begins again. Her dress is shiny and a brilliant blue.

Corn ground, tortillas made, coffee poured, her man eats, packs some more in his bolsa, and is off for the sierra to cut *lena,* wood for the fire, and to look for some cows that have failed to come home. A kitten rubs against Christina's leg as he leaves in the gray light. Then the children rise, eat also, and move down the dirt lane to the highway and the walk into a nearby town for school. The oldest is fifteen, and Christina, her years are hard to measure—perhaps on her face, thirty-five years, perhaps since her birth date, thirty. Now she goes out into the cool air of morning.

The cows must be milked in their wooden corral near the house. Then she goes down to the wash where a bucket dangles over the village's ancient well and she hauls load after load of water to the stock. The day is now on and she pours herself a cup of coffee, and goes to the portals facing the milpa and the wash below, and enjoys the sounds of the forest coming alive. Over her head, the *perico* squawks and she grabs a pole, hoists it up, and the bird hops aboard. The wings have been severely clipped—Christina's mother captured the parrot, trimmed its feathers, and gave it to her as a gift—and the markings show it to be a white fronted parrot. The bird climbs on her shoulder, nuzzles against her hair, and nibbles at her ear. In the brown field below chapotes are in leaf, the big trees a welcome sign of green in the endless brown of the campo as it awaits the rain. In a week or two or three, las aguas will fall, the ground will go wet, life will quicken, and the corn will be planted. Another year will truly begin.

The neighboring hills are being scrapped as more and more of the forest is felled by the village for the planting of buffel grass. Wood also disappears for the cook fires, for the pottery making, for the brick making, for all the warmth that life requires. No one knows the age of this village but its bones and bloodlines testify that it is Indian in origin and winds back into the mists of time. Christina sips her coffee, a young piglet snores at her feet, the parrot chatters in her ear. In the kitchen hangs the haunch of a deer—a fellow villager brought it down off the sierra—and she will cook it today, slow boil it over a wood fire. After that goes in her kitchen, she will put three quarts of milk in her bolsa and walk into town and sell the milk. Then . . . . It hardly matters. The days manage to flow ceaselessly with things to do. Christina sleeps but five hours each night and never rests in the heat of the afternoon.

Ah, Christina's world, if she only knew. There are many conferences about Christina's world now, meetings all over the world concerned with the rapid disappearance of the tropical forest, coalitions dedicated to stopping the people of the world from eating the world. These groups meet in fine buildings with climate controlled air. There are no wood fires at these gatherings and the deer is not in the stew pot. That's the rub, the thing we come back to always after enjoying the beauty of the forest, after being fascinated by the intricacy of the forest. The people of the forest who are eating it root and branch, they to a man, woman, and child are very poor, and they consume very few things of this earth, not nearly as many things as the people who attend the conferences in very distant locations. And yet, their way of life now seems suddenly lethal to all of us. There are so many people now and the earth itself, it does not grow but seems to shrink. So we have this meeting, produce these papers, consider these problems and we always seem to wind up telling the poor they take too much and they look at us, and know they have very little and we have very much.

There will be an answer to this problem—we have no doubt of that. The forest will be gone, dead in a generation if something is not done, and Christina's world of subsistence, babies, cook fires, and deer in the pot will die also if the forest dies. Or we can intervene through some plan, and, armed with money and rules, try to save the forest and then also, the poor will perish if we take away their only source of food, warmth, and home. So we hesitate because the choices become hard and we do not like hard choices. Even worse than a hard choice is the nature of the decision facing us. Not only will Christina have to change . . . we must change also. And we are not used to this, not experienced at all in giving up some of our comforts, in curbing some of our appetites. But we will, but we must or . . . .

For Christina, these concerns do not matter this morning. The sun is up, the parched corn is ground, the tortillas are made, the cows milked and watered, the deer is slow-cooking in the pot, the parrot nibbling at her ear and chattering. She smiles, she smiles so very easily. She will not sleep for fifteen hours but this does not matter either as she looks out at the field ready for the rain and enjoys the calm of God's world under the dark brow of the sierra.

❖

A Calendar

June 24: San Juan's Day. Celebrated in Navojoa, San Bernardo, and elsewhere. The traditional beginning of *las aguas,* the summer rains.

September 16: El Grito, celebration of the first Mexican revolution launched by Father Hidalgo in 1810. Major fiesta in Alamos.

November 2 and 3: The Day of the Dead. Cemeteries and shrines decorated everywhere.

November 13: Procession from Alamos to Aduana, six miles away, to install the Virgin of Balvaneras. Begins at church on Plaza de las Armas around 4 A.M.

November 20: Fiesta for Virgin of Balvaneras in Aduana; ten to twenty thousand people in a village with two to three hundred residents. Some pilgrims walk forty miles.

December: Hecho, *Pachycereus pecten-aboriginum,* begins blooming and continues into spring. A tall columnar cactus at first glance like a saguaro.

December 2–8: Religious observations in Alamos for the Virgin of the Immaculate Conception.

December through February: Amapa blooms with intense clots of pink trees erupting from the increasingly leafless hillsides.

December 12: Virgin of Guadalupe.

December 17–24: Posadas in Alamos reenacting quest by Joseph and the Virgin for a room at an inn.

January 1: Major celebration in Alamos.

January, third week: Major celebration of classical music and song in Alamos with nightly concerts.

February–March: Montezuma cypress, *Taxodium mucronatum*, or sabino, grows new leaves. Tall tree with knobby roots reaching into streams.

February–March: The huge white blooms of *Bombax palmeri* (cuajilote in Spanish) appear on the leafless trees that cling to steep slopes.

March and April: Carnival for lent; Easter observations. Mayo villages around Navojoa feature pascola dancers, and matechines.

May 5: Major fiesta in Alamos for Cinco de Mayo. Horse races.

End of May: The spectacular but brief blooming of *Willardia mexicana* (nesco in Spanish) in which groves of the trees erupt with an intense rose to purple flower. Also the blooming time of Guayacán *(Guaiacum Coulteri)* which is covered with bright blue flowers.

❖

Appendix

N.B.: Species marked with an asterisk (*) are illustrated in *A Handbook of Mexican Roadside Flora* by Charles T. Mason and Patricia B. Mason, 1987.

English	Spanish	Family	Genus	Species
aborigine's comb*	hecho	Cactaceae	*Pachy-cereus*	*pectin-aboriginum*
aguaro	aguaro	Martyniaceae	*Martynia*	*annua*
alder	alamillo	Betulaceae	*Alnus*	*oblong-ifolia*
amapa*	amapa amarilla	Bignoniaceae	*Tabebuia*	*chrysantha*
amapa*	amapa colorada	Bignoniaceae	*Tabebuia*	*palmeri*
Arizona cypress	tascate	Cupressaceae	*Cupressus*	*arizonicus*
Arizona oak	encino blanco	Fagaceae	*Quercus*	*arizonica*
basswood	——	Tiliaceae	*Tilia*	*mexicana*
big-toothed maple	palo de azúcar	Aceraceae	*Acer*	*grandi-dentatum*
boat spine acacia*	guinora, chirowi	Leguminosae	*Acacia*	*cochlia-cantha*
brasil wood*	brasil	Leguminosae	*Haema-toxylon*	*brasiletto*
buffel grass	buffel	Poaceae	*Pennisetum*	*ciliare*
bursera*	torote	Burseraceae	*Bursera*	[various species]
cardinal flower*	——	Lobeliaceae	*Lobelia*	*laxiflora*

English	Spanish	Family	Genus	Species
Chihuahua oak	encino roble	Fagaceae	*Quercus*	*chihuahuensis*
coral bean*	chilicote	Leguminosae	*Erythrina*	*flabelliformis*
cow's horn agave	lechuguilla	Agavaceae	*Agave*	*bovicornuta*
cup leaf oak	encino güeja	Fagaceae	*Quercus*	["mcvaughii"]
desert spoon	sotol	Agavaceae	*Dasylirion*	[new species]
dragon blood	ensangre-grado	Euphorbiaceae	*Jatropha*	*platanifolia*
egg cone pine*	pino blanco	Pinaceae	*Pinus*	*oocarpa*
epiphytic orchid	kiki	Orchidaceae	*Laelia*	*bancilarie*
feather tree*	mauto, mauuto	Leguminosae	*Lysiloma*	*divaricata*
feather tree	tepeguaje	Leguminosae	*Lysiloma*	*microphylla*
fragipani*	suchil, cacalosuchi	Apocynaceae	*Plumeria*	*acutifolia*
goat's beard*	barba de chivato	Leguminosae	*Calliandra*	*houstoniana*
golden cosmos	——	Compositae	*Cosmos*	*sulphureus*
guamuchil*	guamúchil	Leguminosae	*Pithece-llobium*	*dulce*
guasima*	guásima	Stercu-liaceae	*Guazuma*	*ulmifolia*
guayacan*	guayacán	Zygophyl-laceae	*Guaiacum*	*coulteri*
holly	——	Aquifoli-aceae	*Ilex*	*tolucana*
hop bush*	jarilla	Sapindaceae	*Dodonaea*	*viscosa*
hop horn beam	huasimilla	Carpinaceae	*Ostrya*	*virginiana*
kapok*	pochote	Bombacaceae	*Ceiba*	*acuminata*

English	Spanish	Family	Genus	Species
kusi*	kusi	Fagaceae	*Quercus*	*albocincta*
lupine	——	Leguminosae	*Lupinus*	*huachucanus*
madrone	madrono	Ericaceae	*Arbutus*	*arizonica*
madrone*	madrono	Ericaceae	*Arbutus*	*xalapensis*
mesquite	mesquite	Leguminosae	*Prosopis*	*juliflora*
Mexican cottonwood	álamo	Salicaceae	*Populus*	*mexicana*
Mexican jumping bean	brincador	Euphorbiaceae	*Sebastiana*	*pringlei*
Mexican sycamore	aliso	Platanaceae	*Platanus*	*racemosa*
montezuma cypress*	sabino	Taxodiaceae	*Taxodium*	*mucronatum*
morning glory	trompio, other names	Convalvulaceae	*Ipomoea*	[numerous species]
morning glory tree*	palo santo	Convolvulaceae	*Ipomoea*	*arborescens*
mountain muhley	cola de raton	Poaceae	*Muhlenbergia*	*emersleyi*
nesco	nesco	Leguminosae	*Willardia*	*mexicana*
octypus agave	amole	Agavaceae	*Agave*	*vilmoreana*
palo barril*	palo barril	Cochlospermaceae	*Cochlospermum*	*vitifolium*
palo blanco	palo blanco	Leguminosae	*Piscidia*	*mollis*
palo cachora	palo cachora	Olacaceae	*Schoepfia*	*parvifolia*
palo chino	palo chino	Leguminosae	*Pithecellobium*	*mexicanum*
palo colorado	palo colorado	Leguminosae	*Caesalpinia*	*platyloba*
papache*	papache	Rubiaceae	*Randia*	*echinocarpa*

English	Spanish	Family	Genus	Species
rock fig*	tescalama	Moraceae	*Ficus*	*petiolaris*
sahuaro*	sahuaro	Cactaceae	*Cereus*	*giganteus*
scarlet salvia*	salvia roja	Labiatae	*Salvia*	*elegans*
shaving brush tree*	guajilote	Bombacaceae	*Bombax*	*palmeri*
shrubby cassia*	ejotillo del monte	Leguminosae	*Cassia*	*biflora*
silk tassle	——	Garryaceae	*Garrya* *Garrya*	*ovata* *laurifolia*
silver leaf oak	encino	Fagaceae	*Quercus*	*hypoleucoides*
Sonoran persimmon	guaiparin	Ebenaceae	*Diospyros*	*sonorae*
soup bowl oak*	encino güeja	Fagaceae	*Quercus*	*pennivenia*
stinging bush	ortuguilla	Urticaceae	*Urera*	*caracasana*
strangling fig*	nacopuli	Moraceae	*Ficus*	*cotinifolia,* [other species]
sunflower bush*	mirasol	Compositae	*Tithonia*	*calva*
tank bromeliad	mescalito	Bromeliaceae	*Tillandsia*	*cretacea*
tree limber-bush	torote	Euphorbi-aceae	*Jatropha*	*cordata*
tree ocotillo*	torote verde	Fouquieri-aceae	*Fouquieria*	*macdougalii*
tempisque	tempisque	Sapotaceae	*Sideroxylon*	*angustifolium*
tropical hackberry*	garabato	Ulmaceae	*Celtis*	*iguanea*
garambullo*	garambullo	Nyctagi-naceae	*Pisonia*	*capitata*

English	Spanish	Family	Genus	Species
Ures palm	palma	Palmae	*Sabal*	*uresana*
vara prieta	vara prieta	Leguminosae	*Brongni-artia*	*alamosana*
white cottonwood	güérigo	Salicaceae	*Populus*	*monticola*
wild jicama*	jicama	Polygonaceae	*Exogonium*	*bracteatum*
willow-leaved oak	saucillo	Fagaceae	*Quercus*	*viminea*

The Secret Forest was designed by
Emmy Ezzell, produced on the IBM
computer using PageMaker. The text is
set in 11/14 Sabon using Adobe fonts.
It was printed and bound in Japan by
Dai Nippon Printing Co., Ltd.